Fred's Home Companion

Trigonometry

Fred's Home Companion
Trigonometry

Stanley F. Schmidt, Ph.D.

Polka Dot Publishing

ISBN-13: 978-0-9709995-8-0

Library of Congress Catalog Number: 2005905756
Printed and bound in the United States of America

Polka Dot Publishing   Reno Nevada

To order copies of books in the Life of Fred series,

visit our website PolkaDotPublishing.com

Questions or comments? Email Polka Dot Publishing at lifeoffred@yahoo.com

Second printing

        Illustrated by the author with additional clip art furnished under license from Nova
Development Corporation, which holds the copyright to that art.

for Goodness' sake

or as J.S. Bach—who was
never noted for his plain
English—often expressed it:

Ad Majorem Dei Gloriam
(to the greater glory of God)

If you happen to spot an error that the author, the publisher, and the printer missed, please let us know with an e-mail to: lifeoffred@yahoo.com

As a reward, we'll e-mail back to you a list of all the corrections that readers have reported.

What is Fred's Home Companion?

It is lots of things. Since *Life of Fred: Trigonometry* was first published, there have been requests from home schoolers, teachers, and adults who are learning trig. This book is a response to those needs.

Need #1: I'm a home schooler and I would like my trig chopped up into daily bite-sized pieces.

Done! *Fred's Home Companion: Trig* offers you 94 daily readings. In the space of one summer, for example, you can finish all of trig and still have plenty of time to do other things.

Need #2: I'm a classroom teacher and I want someone (like you!) to write out all my lesson plans and lecture notes.

Done! Here are 94 lesson plans. Each one tells you what part of the book you'll be covering. Lots of the lessons include new problems which are not in *LOF: Trig*. These can serve as your lecture notes or as material for pop quizzes or for tests. The answers are also supplied to these problems. The first 79 lessons cover all of trig. The remaining lessons are a review of everything your students will need to know for calculus.

Need #3: I'm an adult working my way through your LOF: Trig book and I'd like the answer key for the end-of-the-chapter problems. In the book you give the answers to half the problems.

Done! Here is the answer key.

Need #4: I'm in need of a lot of practice in trig. Although you have a lot of problems for me to work on in LOF: Trig, I want a bunch more. I really want to pound it into my head.

Done! In this book we supply a ton of additional trig problems. Finish all of these problems in addition to the ones in *Life of Fred: Trig,* and you should be able to join Fred as a professor of mathematics at KITTENS University.

A Note to Students

When you turn to Lesson One in this book, you will find that it asks you to read five pages in *Life of Fred: Trigometry*. Reading a little bit about Fred and his adventures is always a fun way to begin a day. In the first lesson you'll be reading about six-year-old Fred being driven home in a limo that George had ordered for him at the end of *Life of Fred: Advanced Algebra*. On the second page you find the description of the "bit of dinner" that the driver/chef prepared for Fred.

After you have read those five pages, turn back to this book and answer the questions in Lesson One. All the answers are given on the next page, so you'll know you are on the right track.

That's it.

Now to answer some of the common questions that trig students have . . .

WHAT KIND OF CALCULATOR WOULD BE GOOD?

It is time to buy a "scientific calculator" if you don't already own one. It will have **sin, cos, tan, !, log,** and **ln** keys. The most fun key is the "!" key. If you press 8 and then hit the ! key, it will tell you what $8 \times 7 \times 6 \times 5 \times 4 \times 3 \times 2 \times 1$ is equal to. Recently, I saw one on sale for less than $8. That's the last calculator you'll need to learn all the stuff through calculus.*

---

* Some schools require their calculus students to buy a fancy graphing calculator which costs between $80 and $100. I don't own one and I've never needed one. I spent the money I saved on pizza.

WHAT IF I START TO FORGET SOME OF MY ALGEBRA BEFORE I GET TO CALCULUS?

Three answers:

First, trigonometry is a short math course. In 79 lessons you will finish all of trig. If you did 39½ lessons per day, you would be done in two days.*

Second, the *Life of Fred: Trigonometry* book is sometimes used as a pre-calculus book. It includes five chapters that are labeled "Looking Back" and cover major parts of algebra:
- ✓ functions
- ✓ factoring and fractions
- ✓ graphing
- ✓ inverse functions
- ✓ all the number systems (from the natural numbers through the complex numbers)

Third, lessons 80–94 of this *Fred's Home Companion* take you through all the chapters of *Life of Fred: Calculus*, chapter by chapter. A preview of all 24 chapters. We will work on all the things that you will need to remember from arithmetic/algebra/geometry/trig for each chapter of calculus.

For example, chapter four in calculus deals with slope. Lesson 82 in this *Fred's Home Companion* is a final look at the material you learned in algebra and trig about slope.

Our goal is to make you very ready for calculus.

_____

* Other options include: A) two lessons per day which would take you through trig in 39½ days and B) one lesson per day (Monday–Saturday) in which case you would finish in about 13 weeks.

A Note to Parents Who Are Homeschooling Their Kids

Fred's Home Companion will put your children on automatic pilot. Each day they do one (or more) lessons. The reading in *Life of Fred: Trig* is fun. And because it is fun, they will learn mathematics much more easily. You can sit back and watch them learn.

Six-year-old Fred first encounters the need for mathematics in his everyday life, and then we do the math. This is true for all the *Life of Fred* books. The math is *relevant*.

We will see a tiny slice of Fred's life in *LOF: Trig*—from Tuesday evening to Wednesday night—but in those 29 hours Fred does a lot of living. And he does more than just trigonometry problems.

There is a natural way to learn—and an unnatural way. Sticking a large group of kids in a sit-up-straight-and-be-quiet classroom, giving them a dose of English for an hour, then herding them to a math classroom for a dose of math, is asking for trouble.

English teachers teach English. History teachers teach history. Auto shop teachers teach auto shop. But who teaches the kids?

Children (and adults!) love to learn. Watch a bunch of eight-year-olds during the summer playing in the back yard. They find bugs (biology). They dig holes (civil engineering). They wonder why the sun doesn't burn up (nuclear physics). They make mud pies (culinary arts).

One subject tumbles into another. And it is fun.

Life of Fred: Trig aims toward that ideal.

✯ The topic of continuous and discrete variables takes us into a half-page discussion of one of the plays of Shakespeare (p. 37).

✯ When Fred is waiting to see the nurse, he imagines that she will be "a cheerful heir to the legacy of Florence Nightingale." We outline why she played such a pivotal role in the history of women working outside the home (pp. 177–178).

✯ Healthy living is mentioned. *Exercise*: Fred starts his Wednesday morning with "his morning jog around the campus" with the result that "Everything felt so wonderful. He was happy to be alive. . . ." *Diet*: Fred had spent the six years of his life living off vending machine food and pizza with his friends. He has drunk a lot of Sluice during those years—a soda with a lot of sugar in it. He is 36 inches tall and weighs 37 pounds. In the opening two pages of chapter eight, nurse Florrie introduces Fred to a drink that he's never had before. Fred really liked it and exclaimed, "This is great. It quenches your thirst and doesn't leave a nasty aftertaste." And Florrie added, "And no beer gut either." The drink is . . . water. *Dental hygiene*: Each night (p. 29 and p. 262) Fred flosses and brushes his teeth. Preaching about these things ("You should exercise more! You should watch your diet! You should floss!") never seems to work well. But the subliminal message given by Fred's example may do the trick.

★ Learning English is at least as important as learning trig. Fred owns a llama, which he received at his birthday party in chapter six. At the beginning of chapter seven he spots the current issue of a llama magazine. We explain why it is incorrect to say that he was *anxious* to read it.

We spend a half page (p. 184) describing the positive results of reading the great authors.

And we still have plenty of time to cover more trigonometry than is normally presented in a university classroom.

If you would like to visit Fred at his official
Web site and see a complete list of the books that have been
written about him, go to   FredGauss.com

At the Web site you can also order by credit card.

Contents

14

18

Lesson One

Angles of Elevation

Life of Fred:
Trigonometry
pp. 17–21

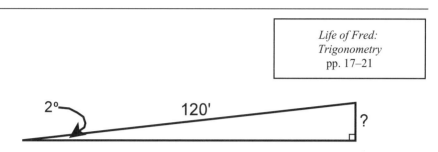

1. In the above triangle the angle of elevation is labeled as 2°. When I measure the angle in my drawing, I find it is actually about 6°. Redraw the triangle more accurately. (Please attempt this first on your own before you look at my answer on the next page.)

The following questions are from geometry.

2. What does the little square in the lower-right-hand corner of the above triangle mean?

3. **Acute angles** are angles that are less than 90°. Draw a right triangle that has an acute angle of 45°. (You are not required to own a protractor. Just use your ruler and make a rough drawing.)

4. Make a drawing of a right triangle in which one of the acute angles is approximately 30°.

5. If one acute angle in a right triangle is 30°, what is the measure of the other acute angle?

6. A theorem from geometry states, "In any 30–60–90 triangle, the side opposite the 30° angle is half of the length of the hypotenuse." In the following diagram, mark the side opposite the 30° angle with "opp" and they hypotenuse with "hyp".

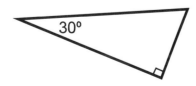

1.

a more
accurate 2°

120'

?

2.  The little square indicates that we are looking at a right angle (= 90°). Triangles which contain a right angle are called right triangles.

3. Your drawing might look like   or like   45°

or like ◁ 45°

The two shorter sides of the triangle (the legs) you draw should have been roughly equal in length.

4. If you want to see how accurately you drew your right triangle containing a 30° angle, measure the shortest side and measure the hypotenuse (the longest side). According to a theorem from geometry, the shortest side in 30° right triangle is exactly half as long as the hypotenuse.

5. The sum of all three angles in *any* triangle is equal to 180°. If one angle is 90° and another is 30°, that would leave 60° for the third angle. These right triangles in which one of the acute angles is 30° are sometimes called 30–60–90 triangles.

6.

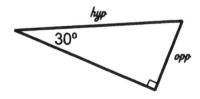

hyp

30°

opp

Lesson Two

Definition of the Sine Function

Do the *Your Turn to Play* starting on p. 22.

Life of Fred: *Trigonometry*   pp. 22–23

1. Find the value of y. Round your answer to the nearest tenth.

2. Find the value of w. Round your answer to the nearest thousandth.

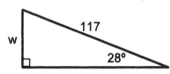

3. Find the value of z. Round your answer to the nearest hundreth.

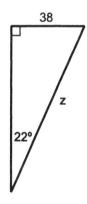

✸A✸N✸S✸W✸E✸R✸S✸

1. $$\sin 34° = \frac{\text{opposite}}{\text{hypotenuse}}$$

    $$\sin 34° = \frac{y}{14}$$

Using the sin key
on a calculator $$0.5591929 = \frac{y}{14}$$

Algebra $$14(0.5591929) = y$$

$$7.8287006 = y$$

Rounding to the
nearest tenth $$7.8 = y$$

2. $$\sin 28° = \frac{\text{opposite}}{\text{hypotenuse}}$$

    $$\sin 28° = \frac{w}{117}$$

    $$0.4694716 = \frac{w}{117}$$
    $$117(0.4694716) = w$$

    $$54.928173 = w$$

    $$54.928 \doteq w \qquad [\text{``} \doteq \text{'' means rounded.}]$$

3.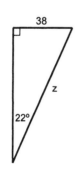

    $$\sin 22° = \frac{\text{opposite}}{\text{hypotenuse}}$$
    $$\sin 22° = \frac{38}{z}$$
    $$0.3746066 = \frac{38}{z}$$
    $$z = \frac{38}{0.3746066}$$

    $$z = 101.43975$$

    $$z \doteq 101.44$$

Lesson Three

Angles of Depression

Do the *Your Turn to Play*.

Life of Fred:
Trigonometry
pp. 24–26

1. Years ago the KITTENS University president had seen a statue  on an Internet auction site and bid $6 for it. Looking at the picture (and failing to read the description) he thought it was just a little clay sculpture that he might put on his desk to remind him of the flat plains of Kansas. To his surprise he won the auction. To his further surprise he found that the shipping cost was $2982.07. That shouldn't have been such a surprise since the camel was taller than the president's mansion.

He told the movers to leave "the thing" at the border of the campus and he would figure out what to do with it later. Later never happened.

The students thought that this monstrous stone statue had been placed at the entrance to the campus by some anonymous donor. They named the statue Cammy.

Joe once remarked to Darlene, "I bet Cammy stands for the thirst for knowledge."

Darlene responded, "Yeah. Sure. You know camels can go a long time without drinking."

After Fred had said "Thank you" to the driver, he turned and started walking toward the entrance to KITTENS University. Fred smiled as he spotted Cammy. Fred's eyes and the camel's knees are both 30" from the ground. As Fred looked down at Cammy's feet, he noticed that the angle of depression was 0.477°. How far was Fred from Cammy?

[Hint: First find the distance from Fred's eyes to Cammy's feet.]

1. Here's the given. The question mark is what we want to find.

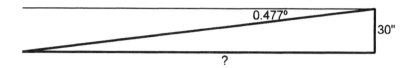

Using alternate interior angles and replacing the question mark with an "x" we have:

The hint suggested that we first find the length of the hypotenuse (r).

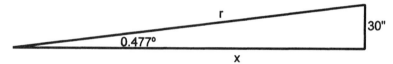

$$\sin 0.477° = \frac{30}{r}$$

$$0.0083251 = \frac{30}{r}$$

$$r = \frac{30}{0.0083251}$$

r = 3603.5498 inches

By the Pythagorean theorem $x^2 + 30^2 = r^2$

$$x^2 + 30^2 = (3603.5498)^2$$
$$x^2 = 12984671$$
$$x = 3603.4249 \text{ inches}$$

If we round off to two significant places (since the height of Fred's eyes was probably accurate to two significant places), we have x = 3600" which is one hundred yards.

Lesson Four

Area of a Triangle = ½ ab sin θ

Do the *Your Turn to Play*.

Life of Fred:
Trigonometry
pp. 27–29

Find the areas of each of these two triangles.

1.

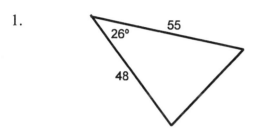

2.

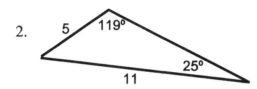

3. There was a proposal to put Cammy at one of the vertices of Kite Lake. The lake covers 1242 square feet. (From geometry we are told that a kite is a quadrilateral—a four-sided polygon—which has two adjacent pairs of congruent sides.) How long is the dashed line from Cammy to the opposite vertex?

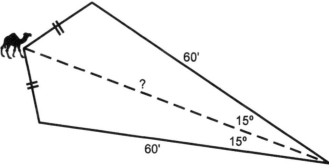

1. A = ½ ab sin θ = ½(48)(55) sin 26°
      = ½(48)(55)(0.4383712) = 578.64991

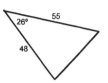

2.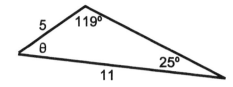

We first need to find θ. Since the sum of the angles of any triangle equals
180°, we have θ + 119° + 25° = 180°.   θ = 36°.

Area = ½ ab sin θ = ½(5)(11) sin 36° = 16.164094

3. Since the area of the
whole lake is 1242
square feet and since
the two triangles are
congruent, the area of
the lower triangle is
621 sq. ft.

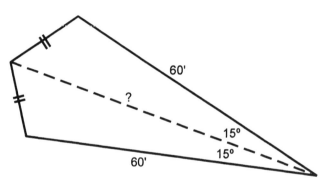

Replace the question mark by b.

Area = ½ ab sin θ

621 = ½ (60)(b) sin 15°

621 = 30b(0.2588191)
79.979 = b

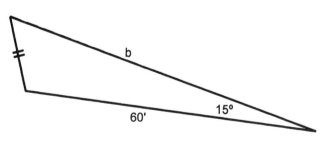

b is approximately 80 feet.

Lesson Five

End of the Chapter—Review & Testing
Part One

Do all the problems in the first two cities.

Life of Fred:
Trigonometry

The Cities starting
on p. 30

Elephant Butte

Harper

Lesson Six

End of the Chapter—Review & Testing
Part Two

Do all the problems in
the second pair of cities.

Life of Fred:
Trigonometry

The Cities starting
on p. 31

Odd answers are in
the text, and even
answers are
given here.

Talpa

Young

EVEN ANSWERS

Talpa

2. 2875.2237 sq meters. Since the given information in the problem was measurements, we could report the answer as 2900 sq meters or 3000 sq meters depending on whether the measurement of 60 meters had two or only one significant digit. (Small discussion: Normally, 60 would be thought of as having one significant digit, just as 700000000 has one significant digit. However, it could be argued that since the other measurement was 117 meters, that whoever was doing the measuring was doing it to the nearest meter. In that case the 60 meter measurement would have two significant digits.)

4. 8594.4062 ft. Since the 45 ft that is given in the original problem is a measurement and since 45 has two significant digits, we should report the distance between the limo and Fred as 8600 ft.

Young

2. 2.13/7.58   4. 1087.964

Lesson Seven

End of the Chapter—Review & Testing
Part Three

Do all the problems in
the third pair of cities.

> *Life of Fred:*
> *Trigonometry*
>
> The Cities starting
> on p. 32

 Igo

Jackson

ⒶⓃⓈⓌⒺⓇⓈ

Igo
1. 35.375352
2. 54.513587
3. 23.473578 sq miles.
Rounding to one significant digit the answer is 20 sq miles.
4. 583.36309
5. 128.78841

Jackson
1. 37.190407
2. 28.793852
3. 461.51532
4. 123.23262
5. 65.982563 and rounding to two significant digits, 66 ft.

Lesson Eight

Graphing and Significant Digits

Do the exercises on p. 39.

Odd answers are in
the text, and even
answers are
given here.

Life of Fred:
Trigonometry
pp. 34–39

EVEN ANSWERS

2. 1   4. 5   6. 4   8. 3   10. 2   12. 2

Additional exercises:

13. The point (–4, 28977) is in what quadrant?
14. What is the abscissa of (–4, 28977)?
15. What is the ordinate of the origin?
16. Find the abscissa of the point P.

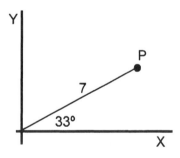

17. What is the ordinate of point P?

13. QII

14. The abscissa is the first coordinate which is –4.

15. The ordinate of a point is its y-coordinate. The y-coordinate of (0, 0) is zero.

16. We want to find the value of x.

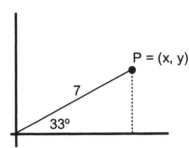

Getting rid of the extra lines:

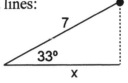

Using the other acute angle:

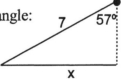

$\sin 57° = \dfrac{x}{7}$

$0.8386706 = \dfrac{x}{7}$

$5.870694 = x$

17. That's even easier than finding the abscissa.

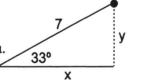

$\sin 33° = \dfrac{y}{7}$

$0.544639 = \dfrac{y}{7}$

$3.8124732 = y$

<h1 style="text-align:center">*Lesson Nine*</h1>

Definition of the Tangent Function

Do the *Your Turn to Play* on p. 43 and on p. 44.

Life of Fred:
Trigonometry
pp. 40–44

1. Find the length of w.

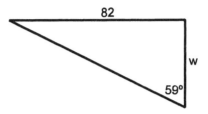

2 When Fred was 100 yards away from Cammy, the angle of elevation from Fred's eyes to the top of Cammy's head was 2.43°. Recall that Fred's eyes and the camel's knees were both 30" from the ground.

   How tall is Cammy?

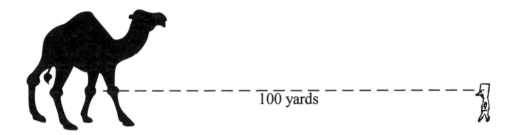

100 yards

3. The official definition of the tangent function: *Start with any angle θ between 0° and 90°. Draw a right triangle where one of the acute angles is equal to θ. Measure the side opposite to θ. Measure the side adjacent to θ. Divide the opposite by the adjacent. This is tan θ.*

   To test your artistic skills: Using the above definition, find the approximate value of tan 30°.

1.

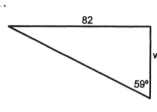

$$\tan \theta = \frac{\text{opposite}}{\text{adjacent}}$$

$$\tan 59° = \frac{82}{w}$$

$$1.6642795 = \frac{82}{w}$$

$$w = \frac{82}{1.6642795}$$

$$w = 49.270571$$

2. $\tan 2.43° = \frac{y}{100}$

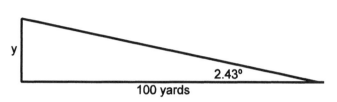

$$0.0424369 = \frac{y}{100}$$

$$4.24369 \text{ yards} = y$$

Converting to inches: $4.24369 \text{ yards} \times \frac{36 \text{ inches}}{1 \text{ yard}} = 152.77284"$.

So the height of Cammy from his knees to his head is 152.77284".

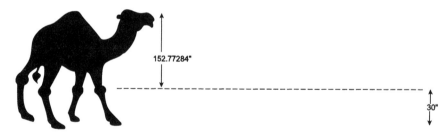

So Cammy's total height is $152.77284 + 30 = 182.77284" \doteq 183"$.

3. Here's my attempt. Yours was probably better.

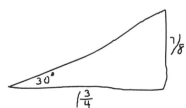

$$7/8 \div 1 \ 3/4 = 7/8 \div 7/4$$
$$= 7/8 \times 4/7 = 1/2 = 0.5$$

Mine would probably have been better if I had used a ruler and a protractor.

Lesson Ten

Slope and the Tangent Function

Do the *Your Turn to Play*.

Life of Fred:
Trigonometry
pp. 45–51

Lesson Eleven

Tangent Problems

Do the *Your Turn to Play*.

Life of Fred:
Trigonometry
pp. 52–55

1. Fred walked up toward Cammy until the
angle of elevation from Fred's feet to Cammy's head was equal to 27°.

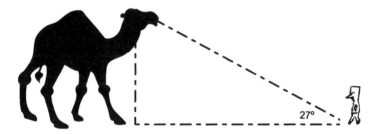

He then walked 133" closer and the angle of elevation became 39°.

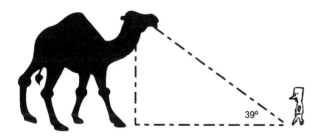

Using these data, determine the height of Cammy.

1.

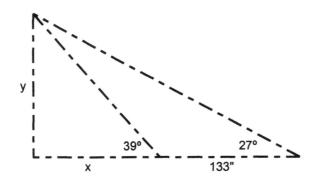

In the triangle on the left:

$$\tan 39° = \frac{y}{x}$$

$$x = \frac{y}{\tan 39°}$$

In the big triangle:

$$\tan 27° = \frac{y}{x + 133}$$

$$x + 133 = \frac{y}{\tan 27°}$$

$$x = \frac{y}{\tan 27°} - 133$$

Combining these two expressions for x:

$$\frac{y}{\tan 39°} = \frac{y}{\tan 27°} - 133$$

$$\frac{y}{\tan 39°} - \frac{y}{\tan 27°} = -133$$

$$y(\frac{1}{\tan 39°} - \frac{1}{\tan 27°}) = -133$$

$$y(\frac{1}{0.809784} - \frac{1}{0.5095255}) = -133$$

$$y(-0.7277134) = -133$$

$$y = 182.76427 \doteq 183"$$

Lesson Twelve

Definition of the Cosine Function

Do the *Your Turn to Play*.

Life of Fred:
Trigonometry
pp. 56–57

1. Look at the official definition of the tangent function (problem 3 on p. 31 of this book). Using that as a guide, write the official definition of the cosine function.

2. Looking at the information on p. 56, how high was the first baseman reaching when she caught the ball? Round your answer to the nearest inch.

$5°$

$90'$

3. Fred warned Betty that she should be careful and not cut herself on his "incredibly sharp honker."

A question that frequently comes up when Fred is discussed in classrooms is, "Just how pointy is his schnoz?"

Suppose we don't have a protractor. We can still find an approximate value for θ if we have a ruler and a calculator.

θ

Using a ruler, measure the lengths for r and x in the diagram below. Then compute the value of cos θ. Finally, try out various angles for θ. Using your calculator, see which cos θ comes closest to the x/r that you just computed.

r

θ

X

✸A✸N✸S✸W✸E✸R✸S✸

1. The official definition of the cosine function: *Start with any angle θ between 0° and 90°. Draw a right triangle where one of the acute angles is equal to θ. Measure the side adjacent to θ. Measure the hypotenuse. Divide the adjacent by the hypotenuse. This is cos θ.*

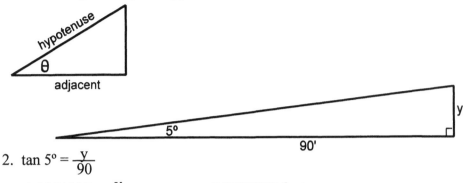

2. $\tan 5° = \dfrac{y}{90}$

$0.0874887 = \dfrac{y}{90}$ $y = 7.8739797$ feet

Converting 7.8739797 feet to inches:

$$7.8739797 \text{ feet} \times \dfrac{12 \text{ inches}}{1 \text{ foot}} = 94.487757" \doteq 94 \text{ inches}$$

3. When I measured, I found r = 4.9 cm. and x = 4.4 cm. If you used a "regular" ruler, you might have gotten x = 1 7/8" and then would have to convert that to 1.875".

$$\cos \theta = \dfrac{x}{r} = \dfrac{4.4}{4.9} \doteq 0.89796$$

Now we need to find what θ will give us cos θ = 0.89796.

We'll try θ = 20°. Then cos θ = 0.9397. That's bigger than 0.89796.

We'll try θ = 15°. Then cos θ = 0.9659. That's even worse.

　　When θ gets smaller, then cos θ gets larger.

We'll try θ = 25°. Then cos θ = 0.9063. That's still bigger than 0.89796, but we're getting closer. We need to increase θ.

We'll try θ = 30°. Then cos θ = 0.8660. That's smaller than 0.89796. We overshot it. θ has to be somewhere between 25° and 30°.

θ = 27°. Then cos θ = 0.8910. That's smaller than 0.89796. Decrease θ.

θ = 26°. Then cos θ = 0.89879. That's larger than 0.89796. Increase θ.

θ = 26.4°. Then cos θ = 0.8957. Decrease θ. As they say on the shampoo bottles, LATHER, RINSE, REPEAT, until you're tired of doing that.

LATHER, RINSE, REPEAT, LATHER, RINSE, REPEAT, LATHER, RINSE, REPEAT, LATHER, RINSE, REPEAT, LATHER, RINSE, REPEAT, LATHER, RINSE, REPEAT. . . .

36

Lesson Thirteen

End of the Chapter—Review & Testing
Part One

Do all the problems in the first two cities.

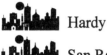 Hardy

San Rafael

> *Life of Fred:*
> *Trigonometry*
>
> The Cities starting
> on p. 58

===========================

Lesson Fourteen

End of the Chapter—Review & Testing
Part Two

Do all the problems in
the second pair of cities.

Odd answers are in
the text, and even
answers are
given here.

 Unity

 Walden

> *Life of Fred:*
> *Trigonometry*
>
> The Cities starting
> on p. 59

✸EVEN✸ ✸ANSWERS✸

Unity

2. 11.616844

4. x

6. By the Pythagorean theorem we find that the hypotenuse is equal to 13. The cosine of the angle is equal to 5/13

Walden

2. 215.57993

4. $\sqrt{34}$

6. tan A = 5/12

Lesson Fifteen

End of the Chapter—Review & Testing
Part Three

Do all the problems in
the third pair of cities.

> *Life of Fred:*
> *Trigonometry*
>
> The Cities starting
> on p. 60

Galene

Index

Galene

1. 14.910381   2. 2403.9691

3. $y = (\tan 7°)x + 9$ or $y = 0.1227846x + 9$

(If the triangle were drawn to the right of Mr. Philistine
instead of to the left, then the equation would be
$y = -0.1227846x + 9$)

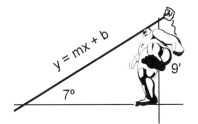

4. 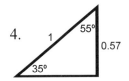 $\sin 35° = \dfrac{0.57}{1}$

                $\cos 55°$ also equals $\dfrac{0.57}{1}$

5.

> cos 0° = 1.00
> cos 20° = 0.94   When you are point-plotting,
> cos 44° = 0.72   you may name any values of x
> cos 68° = 0.37   that you wish. I chose 44° and
> cos 75° = 0.26   68°. You might have chosen
> cos 90° = 0.00   42° and 60°.

6. Two-twelfths of 360° is 60°. cos 60° = 1/2

Index

1. 64.72136   2. 3.1541992

3. This is a 3-4-5 right triangle. tan A = 3/4

4. The tangent of the angle is equal to the slope of the line which is 4.7

5. five feet   6. $y = (\tan 50°)x + 77$ or $y = 1.1917536x + 77$

Lesson Sixteen

Functions Defined As Machines, the Identity Function

Do the two Exercises on p. 63.

Life of Fred:
Trigonometry
pp. 61–63

The odd answer is in the text, and
the even answer is
given here.

2. It probably is a function. The only way it wouldn't be is if a paperclip were somehow manufactured in two different countries or manufactured out in the middle of the ocean, but these scenarios are unlikely.

1. Suppose f was the identity function. Find f(Portugal).

2. Suppose we had the following machine which accepts roosters into its hopper. Whole numbers (= {0, 1, 2, 3, 4, . . . }) are what come out of the machine. Here is how the machine operates.

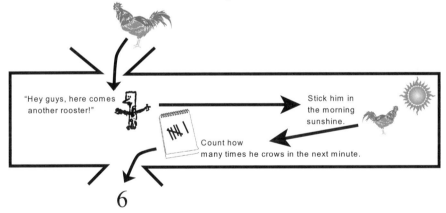

6

Is this machine a function?

3. Would it be a function if we only tossed in dead roosters?

❶❷❸❹❺❻❼❽

1. f(Portugal) = Portugal.

For readers who are into vexillology, here's a picture of Portugal's flag.

It looks like  and is located →

The country on the right of Portugal is Spain.

2. Take a particular rooster. Let's call him Roger. (Roger Rooster is nicely alliterative.) Drop Roger into the machine on January 14th and he gets exposed to the sunshine and crows six times during the next minute. If the name of this machine is g, we would write g(Roger) = 6.

If we drop Roger into the machine on February 2nd, he might only crow four times during the first minute of sunshine. Then g(Roger) = 4.

The definition of function when described as a machine is that for every item we drop into the machine, we will get out exactly one result out of the discharge chute. This wasn't the case with Roger. This machine is not a function.

3. Whenever I drop a dead Roger into my crow-counting machine, I always get the same output from the discharge chute, namely, zero. If the input hopper is restricted to dead roosters, the machine is a function.

Intermission

In geometry we studied If•••then••• statements and their contrapositives.

The contrapositive to *If P then Q* is *If not-Q then not-P*.

An If•••then••• statement is true exactly when its contrapositive is true.

It's an old farmyard saying: "If the rooster is crowing, then it's alive."

In problem 3, we used the contrapositive: "If the rooster isn't alive, it isn't crowing."

Lesson Seventeen

Domain and Range of a Function

Do Exercises 3–8

Odd answers are in
the text, and even
answers are
given here.

Life of Fred:
Trigonometry
pp. 64–66

4. The range of the cosine function is any number strictly between 0 and 1. (Later we will enlarge the domain and range of the cosine function, but right now, when we divide the adjacent side by the hypotenuse, we can only get answers between 0 and 1.)

6. The domain of the tangent function is the set of all angles which could be acute angles in a right triangle. This is the set of all acute angles.

8. The domain of the multiplication function is the set of all pairs of numbers.

Suppose we define the complementary angle function. Call it h. The domain will be all acute angles θ.

Then the domain of h will be $0 < \theta < 90°$.

When θ is thrown into the hopper of h, the art department inside of the machine-function draws a right triangle where one of the acute angles is equal to θ. Then it sends the other acute angle out the discharge chute.

1. h(30°) = ?   2. h(θ) = ?

3. What is the range of h?   4. h(h(20°)) = ?

5. We are now going to redesign the interior of this machine-function so that it will handle a greater variety of items in the hopper. We will enlarge the domain. The important rule is that this newly designed machine will treat all the items in the original domain exactly as it did before. In the original machine we had h(40°) = 50°. In the newly designed machine, we should also have h(40°) = 50°.

In our newly designed machine, instead of having an art department draw the triangle, we will operate under the rule h(θ) = 90 – θ. Find h(10°), h(0°), h(600°) and h(h(56°)).

ANSWERS

1. h(30°) = 60°

2. h(θ) = 90° – θ

3. The range of h is the set of all possible things that can come out of machine h. The domain of h is the set of all acute angles. The complement of any acute angle is also an acute angle. The range of h is the set of all acute angles. h is a function in which its domain is equal to its range.

4. How to deal with h(h(20°))?
Let's just look at the underlined part h(<u>h(20°)</u>). We know the underlined part is equal to 70°. So h(<u>h(20°)</u>) becomes h(70°). And this, in turn, is equal to 20°.

5. h(10°) = 80°
   h(0°) = 90°
   h(600°) = 90 – 600 = –510°
   h(h(56°)) = h(34) = 56°

Intermission

From algebra we know the six-raised-to-the-power function. $6^2 = 36$. $6^3 = 216$. $6^7 = 279,936$. $6^{-1} = 1/6$. $6^{1/2} = \sqrt{6}$. $6^{5/8} = (\sqrt[8]{6})^5$.

We could handle 6^x where x was any rational number. (A rational number is any number which can be written a/b where a and b are integers and b is not zero.)

Now we are going to enlarge the domain of the six-raised-to-the-power function to include any real number. We'll find the value of 6^π.

We will need two rules from logarithms:

i) "The Birdie Rule": $\log c^d = d \log c$
ii) antilog (log x) = x

6^π = antilog (log 6^π) = antilog (π log 6) $\doteq$ antilog (3.14159 × 0.77815) = antilog (2.4446) = 278.36

42

Lesson Eighteen

Trig Angles

Do the *Your Turn to Play*.

Life of Fred:
Trigonometry
pp. 67–68

Lesson Nineteen

Expanding the Domain of a Function

Do the *Your Turn to Play*.

Life of Fred:
Trigonometry
pp. 69–72

1. Let's expand the domain of the tangent function to include 0°. Use your calculator to find the tangent of angles that get closer and closer to 0°. Guess what tan 0° should equal.

2. In problem 3 of the *Your Turn to Play* we expanded the sine function to include 0° in the domain:

$$\sin \theta = \begin{cases} \text{if } 0° < \theta < 90°, \text{ use the old definition involving a right triangle} \\ \text{if } \theta = 0, \text{ then } \sin \theta = 0 \end{cases}$$

Do a similar definition for the tangent function.

3. Discuss why we can (or cannot) repeat problems 1 and 2 for tan 90°.

Lesson Twenty

Trig Functions of Any Angle

Do the *Your Turn to Play*.

Life of Fred:
Trigonometry
pp. 73–78, 80

1. tan 20° = 0.3639702
    tan 5° = 0.0874887
    tan 2° = 0.0349208
    tan 1° = 0.0174551
    tan 0.3° = 0.005236
    tan 0.007° = 0.0001222

    It would be a reasonable guess that tan 0° = 0.

2. This question was almost too easy:
    $$\tan\theta = \begin{cases} \text{if } 0° < \theta < 90°\text{, use the old definition involving a right triangle} \\ \text{if } \theta = 0\text{, then } \tan\theta = 0 \end{cases}$$

3.   tan 84° = 9.51
            tan 89° = 57.29
         tan 89.9° = 572.96
        tan 89.97° = 1909.86
       tan 89.999° = 57295.78

    (We did something very similar to this back on p. 51 in *LOF: Trig*.)
    As θ gets closer and closer to 90°, tan θ gets unbounded large. We can't
    name a number for tan 90°. Any number we name would be too small.

    The upshot is that we can't enlarge the domain of the tangent function
    to include 90°.

Intermission

Now I will contradict myself. I can enlarge the domain
of the tangent function to include 90°. In fact, I can enlarge
any function to include any new elements that were not in
the original domain.

If we start with the tangent function as defined in answer
two directly above, we can add "if θ = 90°, then tan θ = an
egg shell."

And if someone tells you that you can't divide five by
zero—which is the same as saying that (5,0) is not in the
domain of the division function—you can tell them that five
divided by zero equals a white rook.

Maybe it boils down to whether I can define tan 90° in
any kind of *meaningful* way. Who wants egg shells in their
trig functions?

When I defined 6^π two pages ago as equal to 278.35, it
was a smooth and natural definition. It fit right between
$6^{3.14} = 277.58$ and $6^{3.15} = 282.60$.

tan 90°

$\dfrac{5}{0}$

Lesson Twenty-one

Identities from Algebra

Life of Fred:
Trigonometry
pp. 79, 81

1. Which identity from algebra allows me to say that $6x + \xi = \xi + 6x$?

   [ξ (pronounced xi) is my favorite Greek letter.]

2. Why can I say that $wz^5 = z^5w$?

3. What identity from algebra allows me to say $1.34\xi = 1.34\xi$?

Intermission

Six identities are listed in the text on p. 79. The list is not complete. Here are two more:

7. If a = b then b = a   (the symmetric law of equality)
8. If a = b and b = c then a =c
                           (the transitive law of equality)

---

4. If I know that $8\xi = w$, what reason can I give for $w = 8\xi$?

[Xi is the 14th letter of the Greek alphabet. Lower case: ξ. Capital: Ξ.]

5. Supply the reason: $4(\xi + w) = 4\xi + 4w$.

6. Ten revolutions is equal to how many degrees?

7. On p. 81 of the text we are told that we will need a thousand revolutions of θ in order to compute the thousand different answers to the equation $x^{1000} = 7$. (And we will also need the material in chapter ten.)

   Make a guess as to how many revolutions of θ we will need to solve the equation $x^8 = 7$.

8. Find the slope of this line.

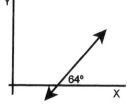

9. How many significant digits are in 0.006?

10. How many significant digits are in 6000.0?

✸A✸N✸S✸W✸E✸R✸S✸

1. The commutative law of addition: a + b = b + a.
2. The commutative law of multiplication: ab = ba.
3. The reflexive law of equality: a = a.
4. The symmetric law of equality: if a = b then b = a.
5. The distributive property: a(b + c) = ab + ac.
6. One revolution is equal to 360°, so ten revolutions equals 3600°.

one
revolution
equals 360°

7. Your guess was correct.*

8. slope = $\dfrac{\text{rise}}{\text{run}}$ = tan 64° ≐ 2.05

rise

64°

run   X

9. 0.006 has one significant digit.

    Start counting with the first non-zero digit.

10. 6000.0 has five significant digits.

    Stop counting with $\begin{cases} \text{the last non-zero digit or} \\ \text{the last gratuitous zero} \end{cases}$

    . . . whichever occurs later

_____

✶ Yes. It is eight. You will also need eight revolutions to solve $x^8 = 5$ and eight revolutions to find the eighth roots of any number.

Lesson Twenty-two

End of the Chapter—Review & Testing
Part One

Do all the problems in the first two cities.

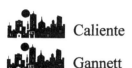 Caliente

Gannett

Life of Fred:
Trigonometry

The Cities starting
on p. 82

Lesson Twenty-three

End of the Chapter—Review & Testing
Part Two

Do all the problems in
the second pair of cities.

Odd answers are in
the text, and even
answers are
given here.

Hamilton

Tampa

Life of Fred:
Trigonometry

The Cities starting
on p. 84

🟊 E V E N 🟊 A N S W E R S 🟊

Hamilton

2. $\{x \mid x = 34° + n(360°)$ where n a natural number less than 41$\}$

4. φ must be equal to 30° (From geometry: the side opposite a 30° angle is half of the hypotenuse.) Therefore, the angle we're looking for is 60°. The cosine is positive in QI and QIV, so θ = 60° and 300°.

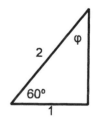

(φ is the Greek letter phi. Sometimes phi is written ϕ.)

47

6. A function is called an **odd function** if, for every x, f(–x) = –f(x). In order to see if y = f(x) = x³ is an odd function, we see if f(–x) equals –f(x):

f(–x) = (–x)³ = –x³

f(x) = x³ so –f(x) = –x³

We note that f(–x) does equal –f(x) and so it is an odd function.

Tampa

2.

4. {x | x = –66° + n(360°) where n is an integer}

6. 180° (and not 360° like the sine and cosine)

Lesson Twenty-four

End of the Chapter—Review & Testing
Part Three

Do all the problems in
the third pair of cities.

Life of Fred:
Trigonometry

The Cities starting
on p. 86

Yountville

Damascus

✦A✦N✦S✦W✦E✦R✦S✦

Yountville

1. 345°

2. 280° + 360°, 280° + 2(360°), 280° + 3(360°),
. . . , 280° + 88(360°)

3. sin θ   tan θ

cos θ

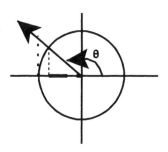

4. Since the sine is positive in QI and QII and since the tangent is positive in QI and QIII, they are both positive in QI.

5. 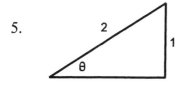 θ must be 30°. Since sin θ is positive, θ will be in either QI or QII. θ = 30°, 150°

6. Yes, since $(-x)^2 = x^2$

7. $y = \tan x$ is *not* an even function. It's an odd function. Using three things that we've already shown (sine is an odd function; cosine is an even function; and tan x = (sin x)/(cos x) for all x) it's easy to show that tan x is odd: tan (–x) = sin(–x)/cos(–x) = (–sin x)/(cos x) = –tan x.

Damascus

1. 90°

2. 38° is in QI

3. $3x + 6$ must be positive. $3x + 6 > 0$ $3x > -6$ $x > -2$

4. 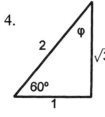 The hypotenuse is equal to 2 by the Pythagorean theorem.

φ must be 30° since the side opposite φ is one-half of the hypotenuse.

In the first quadrant, the angle we're looking for is 60°. However, we're told that tan θ is negative. The tangent is negative in QII and QIV.

So θ = 120° or 300°.

5. $y = x^5$ is odd since $(-x)^5 = -x^5$

6. We are given sin θ = sin (–12°) and we know that sin (–12°) = –sin 12° since the sine is an odd function. Therefore sin θ < 0. The sine is negative in QIII and QIV. The smallest positive value of θ will be in QIII. θ = 192°.

7. Since tan θ = sin θ / cos θ and since sin θ and tan θ are both negative, by algebra we can say that cos θ must be positive.

Lesson Twenty-five

Factoring

Do the exercises.

Odd answers are in
the text, and even
answers are
given here.

Life of Fred:
Trigonometry
pp. 87–89

2. $(\cos x + \sin x)(\cos x - \sin x)$ 4. $(10 + \sin x)(10 - \sin x)$
6. $(\cos^3 x + \tan x)(\cos^3 x - \tan x)$ 8. $(16 \tan^3 x + 2)(16 \tan^3 x - 2)$
10. $(\tan x + 2)(\tan x + 6)$ 12. $(\sin x - 2)(\sin x + 9)$
14. Look for a common factor first. $5(\tan^2 x + 10 \tan x + 25) =$
$5(\tan x + 5)(\tan x + 5)$ 16. $(\sin^2 x + 3)(\sin^2 x + 3)$
18. $(\tan x - \cos x)(\tan^2 x + \tan x \cos x + \cos^2 x)$
20. $(4 \sin x - \tan x)(16 \sin^2 x + 4 \sin x \tan x + \tan^2 x)$
22. $(\cos x + 10)(\cos^2 x - 10 \cos x + 100)$
24. $(\tan^8 x + \cos^3 x)(\tan^{16} x - \tan^8 x \cos^3 x + \cos^6 x)$
26. $(5 \cos x + 2 \sin^2 x)(25 \cos^2 x - 10 \cos x \sin^2 x + 4 \sin^4 x)$

Lesson Twenty-six

Fractions

Do the exercises.

Odd answers are in
the text, and even
answers are
given here.

Life of Fred:
Trigonometry
pp. 90–91

28. $\dfrac{2}{(1 - \cos x)(1 + \cos x)}$ 30. $\dfrac{\tan x \sin x + \cos x}{\sin x}$

32. $\dfrac{\sin^2 x - \sin^2 x \cos^2 x}{\cos^2 x}$

34. $\dfrac{\tan^2 x + 7}{\tan^2 x + 5}$ 36. $\dfrac{2 \cos x - 1}{3 - 2 \sin^2 x}$

Lesson Twenty-seven

Proving Trig Identities—Sines and Cosines

Do the *Your Turn to Play*.

Life of Fred:
Trigonometry
pp. 92–97

1. Go from $\tan x \cos^2 x$ to $\sin x \cos x$.

2. Go from $\dfrac{1 - \cos^2 x}{\tan^2 x}$ to $\cos^2 x$.

3. Factor $27x^3 - 64y^3$.

4. Go from $\dfrac{\sin^3 x - \cos^3 x}{\sin x - \cos x}$ to $1 + \sin x \cos x$.

5. Prove $\dfrac{\sin^2 x + 7 \sin x \cos x + 12 \cos^2 x}{\sin x + 4 \cos x} = \sin x + 3 \cos x$.

1. $\tan x \cos^2 x$

$= \dfrac{\sin x}{\cos x} \cos^2 x$

$= \sin x \cos x$

2. $\dfrac{1 - \cos^2 x}{\tan^2 x}$

$= \dfrac{\sin^2 x}{\tan^2 x}$

$= \dfrac{\sin^2 x}{\left(\dfrac{\sin^2 x}{\cos^2 x}\right)}$

$= \sin^2 x \div \dfrac{\sin^2 x}{\cos^2 x}$

$= \sin^2 x \times \dfrac{\cos^2 x}{\sin^2 x}$

$= \cos^2 x$

3. $27x^3 - 64y^3 = (3x - 4y)(9x^2 + 12xy + 16y^2)$

4. $\dfrac{\sin^3 x - \cos^3 x}{\sin x - \cos x}$

$= \dfrac{(\sin x - \cos x)(\sin^2 x + \sin x \cos x + \cos^2 x)}{\sin x - \cos x}$

$= \sin^2 x + \sin x \cos x + \cos^2 x$

$= 1 + \sin x \cos x$

5. $\dfrac{\sin^2 x + 7 \sin x \cos x + 12 \cos^2 x}{\sin x + 4 \cos x}$

$= \dfrac{(\sin x + 4 \cos x)(\sin x + 3 \cos x)}{\sin x + 4 \cos x}$

$= \sin x + 3 \cos x$

Lesson Twenty-eight

Proving Trig Identities—Secant Function

Do the *Your Turn to Play*.

Life of Fred:
Trigonometry
pp. 98–101

1. Prove $\dfrac{1}{1 - \sin^2 x} = \dfrac{\cos^2 x + \sin^2 x}{\cos^2 x}$

2. Prove $\tan^2 x \cos^2 x = 1 - \cos^2 x$

3. Prove $(\sin^2 x + \cos^2 x)(1 + \tan^2 x) = \dfrac{1}{\cos^2 x}$

1.
$$\frac{1}{1 - \sin^2 x} \overset{?}{=} \frac{\cos^2 x + \sin^2 x}{\cos^2 x}$$

I'm going to work on each side separately.

$$\frac{1}{\cos^2 x} \overset{?}{=} \frac{\cos^2 x}{\cos^2 x} + \frac{\sin^2 x}{\cos^2 x}$$

$$\sec^2 x \overset{?}{=} 1 + \tan^2 x$$
$$\sec^2 x = \sec^2 x$$

A second proof of $\dfrac{1}{1 - \sin^2 x} \overset{?}{=} \dfrac{\cos^2 x + \sin^2 x}{\cos^2 x}$

Again, working each side separately.

$$\frac{1}{\cos^2 x} = \frac{1}{\cos^2 x}$$

Sometimes there are a half dozen different ways to prove an identity.

2. $\tan^2 x \cos^2 x$

$$= \frac{\sin^2 x}{\cos^2 x} \cos^2 x$$

$$= \sin^2 x$$
$$= 1 - \cos^2 x$$

3. $(\sin^2 x + \cos^2 x)(1 + \tan^2 x)$

$$= 1(1 + \tan^2 x)$$
$$= \sec^2 x$$
$$= \frac{1}{\cos^2 x}$$

Lesson Twenty-nine
Proving Trig Identities Using the Five Hints

Do the *Your Turn to Play.*

Life of Fred:
Trigonometry
pp. 102–105

1. Here are the five ways you might approach the proof of a trig identity:

    A) factor the expression
    B) change everything to sines and cosines
    C) add the fractions
    D) work on both sides of the identity
    E) "unadd" the fraction: $\dfrac{a+b}{c}$ would become $\dfrac{a}{c} + \dfrac{b}{c}$

    The second one on the list—B) change everything to sines and cosines—is an approach that will work in a lot of situations, but is not always the shortest approach.

    Show that
$$\frac{1}{\sec^2 x} + \frac{\tan^2 x}{\sec^2 x} = 1 \text{ without using B) change everything to sines and cosines.}$$

2. Establish the identity $\sin^4 x + 6 \sin^2 x \cos^2 x + 5 \cos^4 x = 1 + 4 \cos^2 x$

3. Using   D) work on both sides of the identity
               A) factor the expression
               B) change everything to sines and cosines
and then   C) add the fractions

to establish $\tan x \sin^2 x + \sin x \cos x = \sec x \sin x$.

4. Find the area of

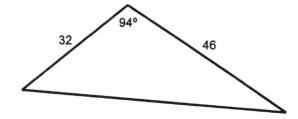

1. $\dfrac{1}{\sec^2 x} + \dfrac{\tan^2 x}{\sec^2 x}$

    $= \dfrac{1 + \tan^2 x}{\sec^2 x}$ Adding the fractions

    $= \dfrac{\sec^2 x}{\sec^2 x}$

    $= 1$

2. $\sin^4 x + 6 \sin^2 x \cos^2 x + 5 \cos^4 x$

                                       This is similar to factoring

    $= (\sin^2 x + 5 \cos^2 x)(\sin^2 x + \cos^2 x)$ $a^4 + 6a^2b^2 + 5b^2$.

    $= (\sin^2 x + 5 \cos^2 x)\, 1$

    $= \sin^2 x + \cos^2 x + 4 \cos^2 x$

    $= 1 + 4 \cos^2 x$

3. $\tan x \sin^2 x + \sin x \cos x \overset{?}{=} \sec x \sin x$ We will work on both sides of the identity.

    $\sin x (\tan x \sin x + \cos x) \overset{?}{=} \sec x \sin x$ Factoring.

    $\sin x \left(\dfrac{\sin x}{\cos x} \sin x + \cos x \right) \overset{?}{=} \dfrac{1}{\cos x} \sin x$ Changing to sines and cosines.

    $\sin x \left(\dfrac{\sin^2 x + \cos^2 x}{\cos x} \right) \overset{?}{=} \dfrac{1}{\cos x} \sin x$ Adding the fractions.

    $\sin x \left(\dfrac{1}{\cos x} \right) \overset{?}{=} \dfrac{1}{\cos x} \sin x$

4. Area $= \frac{1}{2}\, ab \sin \theta = \frac{1}{2} (32)(46)(\sin 94°) \doteq 734.20714$

56

Lesson Thirty

Proving Trig Identities—Cotangent Function

Do the *Your Turn to Play* on p. 106.
Do the *Your Turn to Play* on the top of p. 108.
Do the *Your Turn to Play* on the bottom of p. 108.

> *Life of Fred:*
> *Trigonometry*
> pp. 106–108

(This may look like a lot of *Your Turn to Plays*, but it's only five problems.)

Lesson Thirty-one

Proving Trig Identities—Cosecant Function

> *Life of Fred:*
> *Trigonometry*
> pp. 109–111

Do the *Your Turn to Play*.

1. $\sin 40° = \cos$?
2. $\tan 10° = \cot$?
3. $\sec 20° = $? $(70°)$
4. $\cos 35° = $? $(55°)$
5. In terms of *opposite, adjacent*, and *hypotenuse*, define secant.
6. In terms of *opposite, adjacent*, and *hypotenuse*, define cotangent.
7. What number does not have a reciprocal?

1. $\sin 40° = \cos 50°$
2. $\tan 10° = \cot 80°$
3. $\sec 20° = \csc 70°$
4. $\cos 35° = \sin 55°$
5. The secant is the reciprocal* of the cosine. Since cosine is defined as $\dfrac{\text{adjacent}}{\text{hypotenuse}}$ we would define secant as $\dfrac{\text{hypotenuse}}{\text{adjacent}}$

6. Cotangent is the reciprocal of the tangent.

$$\text{cotangent} = \frac{\text{adjacent}}{\text{opposite}}$$

7. The number zero can be written as $\dfrac{0}{1}$

   It's reciprocal, if it had one, would be $\dfrac{1}{0}$ but since we can't divide by zero, we say that zero doesn't have a reciprocal.

Intermission

Ornery people don't like being told, "You can't divide by zero." In fact, many people who are not cantankerous don't like the idea that you can't divide by zero.

If we took a vote, probably most of the six billion people on the planet would censure mathematicians because they say that you can't divide by zero.

Why all this animadversion? People don't objurgate English teachers when they say that *Dorfy sandlefluffs resist blibbing* is nonsense. Why do they take offense when mathematicians say that division by zero is nonsense?

The truth of the matter is that we mathematicians just can't figure out what the answer would be if you divided a number like, say, 3 by zero. For a moment suppose that 3 divided by zero were equal to 8827.

Suppose $\dfrac{3}{0}$ = 8827.

Then if you multiplied both sides by zero and canceled you would get $0\dfrac{3}{0}$ = 0(8827)

which is   3 = 0. That's pretty hard to live with.

And this argument shows that $\dfrac{3}{0}$ couldn't equal *any* number.

---

* The reciprocal of, for example, 2/3 is 3/2.

Lesson Thirty-two

The Last Hints for Proving Trig Identities

Do the *Your Turn to Play*.

Life of Fred:
Trigonometry
pp. 112–117

1. Establish $\dfrac{1 + \cot^2 x}{1 - \cos^2 x} = \dfrac{\csc^2 x}{\sin^2 x}$

2. Here's one where the artificial cross-multiplying may be the easiest approach:

$$\frac{\cos^2 x \,(\sec x + 1)}{\sin x} = \frac{\sin x}{\sec x - 1}$$

==

Lesson Thirty-three

End of the Chapter—Review & Testing
Part One

Do all the problems in the first two cities.

Life of Fred:
Trigonometry

The Cities starting
on p. 118

 Calistoga

Elma

==

Lesson Thirty-four

End of the Chapter—Review & Testing
Part Two

Do all the problems in
the second pair of cities.

Life of Fred:
Trigonometry

The Cities starting
on p. 119

Even answers are
given on the bottom of
the next page.

 Hamden

University City

1. $\dfrac{1 + \cot^2 x}{1 - \cos^2 x} \overset{?}{=} \dfrac{\csc^2 x}{\sin^2 x}$

   $\dfrac{\csc^2 x}{\sin^2 x}$

   I love them when they're only one step long. You didn't need to artificially cross-multiply, although that would have (eventually) worked also.

2. $\dfrac{\cos^2 x\,(\sec x + 1)}{\sin x} \overset{?}{=} \dfrac{\sin x}{\sec x - 1}$

   $\dfrac{\cos^2 x\,(\sec x + 1)}{\sin x} \left(\dfrac{\sec x - 1}{\sin x} \quad \dfrac{\sin x}{\sec x - 1} \right) \overset{?}{=} \dfrac{\sin x}{\sec x - 1}$

   ·· ····················
   Combining these two   Leaving this alone

   $\dfrac{\cos^2 x\,(\sec^2 x - 1)}{\sin^2 x} \qquad \dfrac{\sin x}{\sec x - 1} \overset{?}{=} \dfrac{\sin x}{\sec x - 1}$

   $\dfrac{\cos^2 x\,(\tan^2 x)}{\sin^2 x} \qquad \dfrac{\sin x}{\sec x - 1} \overset{?}{=} \dfrac{\sin x}{\sec x - 1}$

   $\dfrac{\cos^2 x \sin^2 x}{\sin^2 x \cos^2 x} \qquad \dfrac{\sin x}{\sec x - 1} \overset{?}{=} \dfrac{\sin x}{\sec x - 1}$

   $1 \qquad\qquad \dfrac{\sin x}{\sec x - 1} = \dfrac{\sin x}{\sec x - 1}$

Hamden

2. $\dfrac{\cos^2 x + \tan^2 x - 1}{\sin^2 x} = \tan^2 x$

   $\dfrac{\cos^2 x - 1}{\sin^2 x} + \dfrac{\tan^2 x}{\sin^2 x}$

   $\dfrac{-\sin^2 x}{\sin^2 x} + \sec^2 x$

   $-1 + \sec^2 x$

4. $\cot^2 x - \cos^2 x = \cot^2 x \cos^2 x$

   $(\cos^2 x / \sin^2 x) - \cos^2 x$

$$\frac{\cos^2 x - \sin^2 x \cos^2 x}{\sin^2 x}$$

$$\frac{\cos^2 x (1 - \sin^2 x)}{\sin^2 x}$$

$$\frac{\cos^2 x \, (\cos^2 x)}{\sin^2 x}$$

University City

2. $\dfrac{\sin^2 x}{1 - 2\cos x - 3\cos^2 x} = \dfrac{1 - \cos x}{1 - 3\cos x}$

$$\frac{1 - \cos^2 x}{1 - 2\cos x - 3\cos^2 x}$$

$$\frac{(1 + \cos x)(1 - \cos x)}{(1 + \cos x)(1 - 3\cos x)}$$

4. $\dfrac{\cot^2 x - \cos^2 x}{\cos^2 x} = \cot^2 x$

$$\frac{\cot^2 x}{\cos^2 x} - 1$$

$$\frac{1}{\sin^2 x} - 1$$

$$\csc^2 x - 1$$

====

Lesson Thirty-five

End of the Chapter—Review & Testing
Part Three

Do all the problems in
the third pair of cities.

Life of Fred:
Trigonometry

The Cities starting
on p. 120

 Zearing

 Indian Peak

❂ANSWERS❂

Zearing

1. $\dfrac{\cos x}{\cot x - 3\cos x}$ $= \dfrac{1}{\csc x - 3}$

$\dfrac{\cos x}{(\cos x/\sin x) - 3\cos x}$

$\dfrac{\cos x}{\cos x(\,(1/\sin x) - 3)}$

2. $\sec^2 x + \csc^2 x$ $= \sec^2 x \csc^2 x$

$(1/\cos^2 x) + (1/\sin^2 x)$

$\dfrac{\sin^2 x + \cos^2 x}{\sin^2 x \cos^2 x}$

$\dfrac{1}{\sin^2 x \cos^2 x}$

3. $\cos^2 x + \tan^2 x + \sin^2 x$ $= \sec^2 x$

$1 + \tan^2 x$

$\sec^2 x$

4. $\dfrac{\sin^4 x - \cos^4 x}{\sin^2 x - \cos^2 x}$ $= 1$

$\dfrac{(\sin^2 x + \cos^2 x)(\sin^2 x - \cos^2 x)}{\sin^2 x - \cos^2 x}$

5. $\dfrac{1 - \sin x}{\cos x}$ $\overset{?}{=} \dfrac{\cos x}{1 + \sin x}$

$\dfrac{1 - \sin x}{\cos x} \left(\dfrac{\mathbf{1 + \sin x}}{\mathbf{\cos x}} \quad \dfrac{\mathbf{\cos x}}{\mathbf{1 + \sin x}} \right)$

$\dfrac{(1 - \sin^2 x)}{\cos^2 x} \qquad \dfrac{\cos x}{1 + \sin x}$

$1 \quad \dfrac{\cos x}{1 + \sin x}$

Indian Peak

1. $\dfrac{\sec^2 x}{\sin^2 x} \overset{?}{=} \dfrac{1}{\sin^2 x - \sin^4 x}$ $\qquad$ Working on both sides.

$\dfrac{1/\cos^2 x}{\sin^2 x} \overset{?}{=} \dfrac{1}{\sin^2 x(1 - \sin^2 x)}$

$\dfrac{1}{\sin^2 x \cos^2 x} = \dfrac{1}{\sin^2 x \cos^2 x}$

62

2. $\dfrac{2 \cos^2 x + 5}{2 \cos x + 5 \sec x}$ = cos x

$\dfrac{2 \cos^2 x + 5}{2 \cos x + 5(1/\cos x)}$

$\dfrac{\cos x \, (2 \cos^2 x + 5)}{2 \cos^2 x + 5}$ Multiplying top and bottom by cos x to eliminate the complex fraction.

3. cos x + tan x sin x   =   sec x

$\cos x + \dfrac{\sin^2 x}{\cos x}$

$\dfrac{\cos^2 x + \sin^2 x}{\cos x}$

$\dfrac{1}{\cos x}$

4. $\dfrac{1 - \sin^2 x}{1 + \cot^2 x}$ = $\sin^2 x \cos^2 x$

$\dfrac{\cos^2 x}{\csc^2 x}$

$\sin^2 x \cos^2 x$

5. $\dfrac{1 + \cot^3 x}{1 + \cot x}$ = $\csc^2 x - \cot x$

$\dfrac{(1 + \cot x)(1 - \cot x + \cot^2 x)}{1 + \cot x}$

$1 - \cot x + \cot^2 x$

$\csc^2 x - \cot x$

======================================

Lesson Thirty-six

Graphing y = a sin (bx + c)

Do the Exercises on p. 126

Life of Fred:
Trigonometry
pp. 121–126

Odd answers are in the
text, and even answers are
given on the next page.

2. The graph of y = 20 cot ((½)x + 300º) is twenty times as tall as y = cot x.

It is half as "fast"—it is stretched horizontally twice as much as y = cot x.

It is shifted 300º to the left.

4. y = ½ cos x

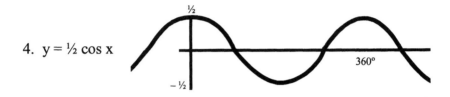

6. cos x = sin (90º + x)

Intermission

Many students (and teachers!) consider Chapter 4 (Proving Trig Identities) to be the hardest part of trigonometry.

Being difficult does not necessarily mean that it is bad. It means that proving an identity was not just a mechanical procedure that any dumb computer could do.

When you played Fred's board game, Saltimrazzo, there was no fixed way to establish the identities. Sometimes you needed to factor, and sometimes you needed to multiply things out. It reminds me of the third chapter of Ecclesiastes: *There is a time for killing and a time for healing; a time for laughter and a time for mourning.* (verse 3).

Proving trig identities is a bit like life: there is no fixed procedure and ingenuity is often required if you are to succeed.

That is why establishing identities is my favorite part of trig.

Lesson Thirty-seven

Degrees, Minutes, Seconds

Do the *Your Turn to Play*.

> *Life of Fred:*
> *Trigonometry*
> pp. 127–129

1. Back in Lesson Nine, Fred was 100 yards
away from Cammy and the angle of elevation from Fred's eyes to the top
of Cammy's head was 2.43°.

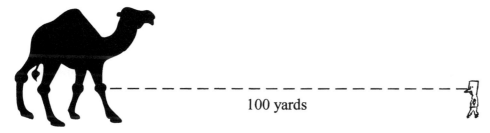

We computed that the height of Cammy from his knees to his head is
152.77284".

Now, instead of using a right triangle, we will use a circle of radius
100 yards. Cammy (from knees to head) subtends an angle of 2.43° in
Fred's eye. What part of the circumference of the circle does Cammy
(from knees to head) occupy?

2. Convert 1.72° into degrees, minutes and seconds.

1. Using the right triangle we were looking for the value of y.

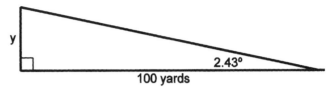

Using a circle we are looking for the value of s.

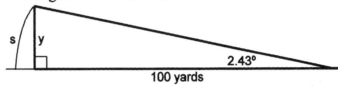

The curved length of s looks longer than the length of y. It is. However, my drawing isn't quite accurate. I have labeled the angle as 2.43°, but it is more like 20°. If I drew the picture more precisely, it might look like this:

We computed that y = 152.77284". Now we will compute how long the arc length s is.

The radius = 100 yards. The diameter = 200 yards. The circumference of the circle = 200π yards.

We want $\dfrac{2.43°}{360°}$ part of that circumference.

$$s = \frac{2.43°}{360°} \times 200\pi \doteq 4.241150 \text{ yards} = 152.68149"$$

s and y are about a tenth of an inch apart. (0.09144")

2. 1.72°
   = 1° + 0.72°
   = 1° + 0.72° × $\dfrac{60'}{1°}$
   = 1° + 43.2'
   = 1° + 43' + 0.2'
   = 1° + 43' + 0.2' × $\dfrac{60"}{1'}$
   = 1° + 43' + 12"

Lesson Thirty-eight

Radians

Do the *Your Turn to Play*.

Life of Fred:
Trigonometry
pp. 130–133

1. Sometimes in the middle of the night, things look a little different. You hold up your hand in the dark and look at it. You think, Five fingers. What an odd number. That just doesn't look right. Every duck I know—like Donald or Daisy—have four fingers on each hand. Duck hands make a lot more sense than people hands.

If we had duck hands, we would use the base-eight system and we could count 1, 2, 3, 4, 5, 6, 7, 10, 11, 12, 13, 14, 15, 16, 17, 20, 21. . . .

In duck base-eight, 23 means two eights and three ones.
In decimal (base-ten) 23 means two tens and three ones.

How lucky ducks are when they go bowling. They don't waste so many fingers when they hold a bowling ball.

wasted fingers

And I could have skipped a year of elementary school since the multiplication tables only go up to 7 × 7.

Fill out the duck base-eight multiplication table.

	1	2	3	4	5	6	7
1							
2		4	6	10			
3							
4					24		
5							
6							52
7							

[Six times seven is 42 which in base-eight is five 8s and two 1s.]

1.

	1	2	3	4	5	6	7
1	1	2	3	4	5	6	7
2	2	4	6	10	12	14	16
3	3	6	11	14	17	22	25
4	4	10	14	20	24	30	34
5	5	12	17	24	31	36	43
6	6	14	22	30	36	44	52
7	7	16	25	34	43	52	61

Intermission

It's easy to see the advantages of using a base-eight system. The multiplication (and addition) tables are smaller. There is less to memorize.
Are there any disadvantages?

If there weren't any drawbacks to using a base-eight system, then a base-six system would be even better.
And a base-two system would be the best.

But there is an inconvenience. With a smaller base system the numbers get longer.
999 in base ten (= 9 hundreds + 9 tens + 9 ones) would equal 1747 in base eight (= 1 *512s* + 7 *64s* + 4 *8s* + 7 *1s.*)

And in base two, 999 would be written 1111100111 which is quite a mouthful. (= 1 *512s* + 1 *256s* + 1 *128s* + 1 *64s* + 1 *32s* + 0 *16s* + 0 *8s* + 1 *4s* + 1 *2s* + 1 *1s.*)

multiplication
table in base two

Lesson Thirty-nine
Area of a Sector

Do the *Your Turn to Play* on p. 135.
Do the *Your Turn to Play* on p. 137.

Life of Fred:
Trigonometry
pp. 134–137

1. Suppose your calculator only worked in degrees and not in radians. How would you find sin 0.76?

2. Find θ to the nearest degree. The area of the sector is 11.1177.

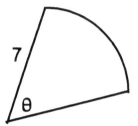

3. The area of this triangle is 38.04. To the nearest one-hundredth, find the approximate value of θ in radians. (Hint: You will need to do some trial and error on your calculator.)

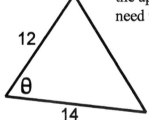

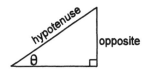

1. First, convert 0.76 to degrees. $0.76 \times \dfrac{180°}{\pi} \doteq 43.5444792°$.
Then $\sin 43.5444792° = 0.6889215$.

2. Area = $(\frac{1}{2})r^2\theta$

    $11.1177 = (\frac{1}{2})(49)\theta$

    $\theta = 0.4537837$ (This is in radians.)

    $\theta = 0.4537837 \times \dfrac{180°}{\pi} = 25.999889° \doteq 26°$

3. Area of a triangle (from Chapter 1): $A = \frac{1}{2}\, ab \sin \theta$. This formula is good when θ is expressed either in degrees or radians.

    We know $A = 38.04$, $a = 12$, $b = 14$.
    $38.04 = \frac{1}{2}\,(12)(14) \sin \theta$
    $\sin \theta = 0.4528571$

    I put my calculator in radian mode and try to make $\sin \theta = \underline{0.4528571}$.

First try:	$\sin 0.2 = 0.1986693$	I just chose 0.2 as a guess. It was too low.
Next try:	$\sin 0.3 = 0.2955202$	Still too low.
Next try:	$\sin 0.5 = 0.4794255$	0.5 is too high.
Next try:	$\sin 0.45 = 0.4349655$	I'm getting there. Too low.
Next try:	$\sin 0.47 = 0.4528863$	Just the tiniest bit too high..
Next try:	$\sin 0.46 = 0.4439481$	So the answer is somewhere between 0.46 and 0.47.

$\theta = 0.47$ gives a much better answer than $\theta = 0.46$.

Intermission

There is a secret method of finding θ when you know that $\sin \theta = 0.4528571$.

Normally, we know the angle θ and we want to find the value of $\dfrac{\text{opposite}}{\text{hypotenuse}}$. We use the sine function.

Give me an angle and the sine function will give me a ratio. We can also make the sine function go backwards —give me the ratio and I can find θ. It's called the *inverse function*.

If I enter 0.4528571 in my calculator and then use the $\sin^{-1}$ key, I get 0.4699673 (if I'm in radian mode).

One step. No trial-and-error. Very neat and clean. But I'm not allowed to mention the inverse sine function until Chapter 8.

The $\sin^{-1}$ key is usually activated by hitting a colored key marked "2nd" or "alt" and then the sin key.

Lesson Forty
End of the Chapter—Review & Testing
Part One

Do all the problems in the first two cities.

Life of Fred: Trigonometry

The Cities starting on p. 138

![Calpet icon] Calpet

![Gardena icon] Gardena

Lesson Forty-one
End of the Chapter—Review & Testing
Part Two

Do all the problems in
the second pair of cities.

Life of Fred: Trigonometry

The Cities starting on p. 139

Odd answers are in
the text, and even
answers are
given here. ⬇

 San Simeon

 Waldo

EVEN ANSWERS

San Simeon
2. 5° 59' 10.644"
4. 21° is larger. 21° ≈ 0.3665191

Waldo
2. 0.0107888 is larger. (37' ≈ 0.0107629)
4. 2793 miles

Lesson Forty-two

End of the Chapter—Review & Testing
Part Three

Do all the problems in
the third pair of cities.

> *Life of Fred:*
> *Trigonometry*
>
> The Cities starting
> on p. 140

 Yuba City

 Damon

ⓐⓝⓢⓦⓔⓡⓢ

Yuba City
1. 26°
2. 77° 5' 34.728"
3. 0.00001 is larger (2" ≈ 0.0005556° ≈ 0.0000097)
4. 2434 square miles
5. 1047 miles

Damon
1. 69.81317 or 200π/9
2. 44° 42' 18.324"
3. 87 inches
4. 0.0000048
5. 0.48/2π
6. The area of a sector is ½ r²θ.
   The area of a triangle is ½ r²sin θ.
   The difference gives us the area of a segment: A = ½ r²θ − ½ r²sin θ.

   This is sometimes written A = ½ r²(θ − sin θ).

Lesson Forty-three
Conditional Trig Equations

Life of Fred:
Trigonometry
pp. 141–147

1. The first perfect number is 6. The second perfect number is less than 100. Find it.

2. In algebra we had identities and conditional equations. Classify each of these as either an identity or a conditional equation:
   A) $6x + 2 = 26$
   B) $x(y + z) = xy + xz$
   C) $x + x + x = 3x$
   D) $\sqrt{x + 7} = 12$
   E) $\log_5 25 = x$

3. $x = x$ is always true and therefore is an identity.
   $x = x + x$ is sometimes true and therefore is a conditional equation.
   What about $x = x + 1$?

Do the *Your Turn to Play* on p. 147.

Lesson Forty-four
Nine Formulas for Functions of Two Angles

Life of Fred:
Trigonometry
pp. 148–154

Do the *Your Turn to Play* on p. 152. (One problem.)
Do the *Your Turn to Play* on p. 153. (One problem.)
Do the *Your Turn to Play* on p. 154. (Four problems.)

1. The divisors of 28 are 1, 2, 4, 7, 14.
   $1 + 2 + 4 + 7 + 14 = 28.$

2. A) $6x + 2 = 26$ is a conditional equation. Not every value of x makes it true. In fact, in this case, only one value of x makes it true.

   B) $x(y + z) = xy + xz$ is an identity. Every value of x, y, and z make this true. (In algebra we called this the distributive property.)

   C) $x + x + x = 3x$ is an identity. It is true for every value of x.

   D) $\sqrt{x + 7} = 12$ is a conditional equation.

   E) $\log_5 25 = x$ is a conditional equation. By one of the definitions of logarithms it is equivalent to $5^x = 25$ which is only true when $x = 2$.

3. $x = x + 1$ is never true. It is a conditional equation. We did *not* define a conditional equation as an equation that is sometimes true and sometimes false. We defined it as an equation that is not always true.

Do the *Your Turn to Play*.

Life of Fred:
Trigonometry
pp. 155–158

1. In the first example on p. 157 we read:

☞For example, to show that $\sin^2 E = \frac{1}{2} - \frac{1}{2} \cos 2E$, you look higher on the list and find $\sin C \sin D = \frac{1}{2}(\cos (C - D) - \cos (C + D))$. Just letting C and D both equal E, you're done.

Using that as a model, prove

$$\cos^2 E = \frac{1}{2} + \frac{1}{2} \cos 2E$$

2. Prove the double-angle formula

$$\tan 2\theta = \frac{2 \tan \theta}{1 - \tan^2 \theta}$$

Intermission

Would you like to make your math career "solitary, poor, nasty, brutish, and short"?

Just spend your time memorizing all these million trig formulas.

Even after you have memorized them, you will probably forget them next week.

I've marked the two pages of formulas in the text with flowers so that if you ever need any of those formulas, you will be able to find them more easily. The formulas should be as pleasant as flowers.

Formulas, like flowers, are designed to be looked at and smelled, but not eaten. (With minor exceptions.)

Suppose, a couple of years from now, you are working in a Trigonometry Factory. Your boss comes to you and wants you to do a problem involving trig functions of two angles.

Will your boss tell you, "Now shut your book and take this paper and do the problem"? No, of course not.

You will take the problem, head to your office, open up your *Life of Fred: Trig* book to the page with the flowers.

I have taught trig in various high school and college settings for years. I have written two books on trigonometry. I have a Ph.D. in math. I have never memorized what sin C sin D equals.

1. To prove $\cos^2 E = \frac{1}{2} + \frac{1}{2} \cos 2E$.

Above $\cos^2 E = \frac{1}{2} + \frac{1}{2} \cos 2E$ on the list
is the formula $\cos C \cos D = \frac{1}{2}(\cos (C - D) + \cos (C + D))$.
   Let C and D both equal E and we obtain
$$\cos E \cos E = \frac{1}{2}(\cos (E - E) + \cos (E + E)$$
which simplifies to
$$\cos^2 E = \frac{1}{2}(\cos 0 + \cos 2E)$$
and since $\cos 0 = 1$,
$$\cos^2 E = \frac{1}{2}(1 + \cos 2E)$$
$$\cos^2 E = \frac{1}{2} + \frac{1}{2} \cos 2E$$

2. To prove $\tan 2\theta = \dfrac{2 \tan \theta}{1 - \tan^2 \theta}$

Above $\tan 2\theta = \dfrac{2 \tan \theta}{1 - \tan^2 \theta}$ on the list

is the formula $\tan (x + y) = \dfrac{\tan x + \tan y}{1 - \tan x \tan y}$

Let both x and y equal θ and we obtain

$$\tan (\theta + \theta) = \dfrac{\tan \theta + \tan \theta}{1 - \tan \theta \tan \theta}$$

$$\tan 2\theta = \dfrac{2 \tan \theta}{1 - \tan^2 \theta}$$

Intermission

The quote on the previous page ("solitary, poor, nasty, brutish, and short") is Thomas Hobbes' description of life.

Hobbes was born in England in 1588. Another famous phrase of his is: "All mankind [is in] a perpetual and restless desire for power." His pessimism saw a "war of every man against every man."

I bet his teacher made him memorize all those trig formulas.

Lesson Forty-six
Proof of sin (x + y) = sin x cos y + cos x sin y

Do the *Your Turn to Play*.

Life of Fred:
Trigonometry
pp. 159–164

Lesson Forty-seven
End of the Chapter—Review & Testing
Part One

Do all the problems in the first two cities.

Life of Fred:
Trigonometry

The Cities starting
on p. 165

Ellsworth

Dalton

Lesson Forty-eight
End of the Chapter—Review & Testing
Part Two

Do all the problems in
the second pair of cities.

Life of Fred:
Trigonometry

The Cities starting
on p. 166

Odd answers are in
the text, and even
answers are
given here.

 Queenstown

 Upland

★ E V E N ★ ★ A N S W E R S ★

Queenstown
2. 89°, 91°, 269°   4. π/6, π/2, 5π/6, 3π/2

Upland
2. 180° or π   4. 45° or π/4

Lesson Forty-nine

End of the Chapter—Review & Testing
Part Three

Do all the problems in
the third pair of cities.

Life of Fred:
Trigonometry

The Cities starting
on p. 167

 Yukon

 Kalamazoo

---

✪N✪W✪R✪

Yukon
1. x = 135°, 315° or x = 3π/4, 7π/4
2. 10°, 170°, 190°
3. x = π/12
4. θ = 30° or π/6
5. sin (x − y)
   = sin (x + (−y))
   = sin x cos (−y) + cos x sin (−y)
   = sin x cos y − cos x sin y

Kalamazoo
1. x = 90° or x = π/2
2. 360° or 2π
3. x = 20°
4. x = 42°
5. Starting with cos C cos D = ½(cos (C − D) + cos (C + D))
Let C = x and let D = x.
This yields cos x cos x = ½(cos (x − x) + cos 2x)) = ½(1 + cos 2x).

Lesson Fifty

Picking a Number at Random

Do the *Your Turn to Play*.

> *Life of Fred:*
> *Trigonometry*
> pp. 168–171

1. Suppose someone asks you to pick a number between one and ten. If you truly selected a number at random, what are the chances it would be seven?

2. Each box of Wizzo Cereal is marked "18 oz." What is the probability

that a box of Wizzo contains exactly 18 ounces of cereal?

3. Jan is the cashier at Waddles Doughnuts and isn't very good at making change. Give Jan a $10 bill and you might get any amount of change from 1¢ to $9.99—completely chosen at random.

What is the probability that if you give Jan a $10 bill you will receive $5.27 in change?

4. 30° is how many radians?

5. You are given a big trig equation and you are asked whether it is an identity or a conditional equation.

Maybe something like:

$$\frac{\tan^3 x - \cot^3 x}{\tan x - \cot x} - \sec^2 x + \cos^2 x - \cot^2 x + \sin^4 x - \frac{\sin^4 x - \cos^4 x}{1 - \cot^4 x} + \sin^2 x = 1$$

What might be the easiest way to make a quick guess as to whether it's an identity or a conditional equation?

1. If it is to be *any number* between one and ten, there are millions (1,000,000s) or billions (1,000,000,000s) of possible answers.

   If all the possible numbers were equally likely to be picked (which is the definition of *random*) then you are just as likely to pick 7 as you would be to pick 7.00000000000000000000000001 or 7.0000000000000000002 or 7.0000000000000000003. There are a zillion numbers that are very close to 7. The chances of picking 7 (exactly) is virtually zero.

2. A box selected at random might weigh 17.9999999993989 or it might weigh 18.000000000000397923699. The chances of it weighing exactly 18 ounces is zero.

3. The difference between this problem and the previous two problems is that change is a variable that is **discrete**. You might receive 1¢ or 2¢ or 3¢, but you won't receive 2.8756¢.

   Variables like weight, length or time are **continuous** variables.

   The probability of receiving exactly $5.27 is one chance in 999.

4. 30° is $\pi/6$ radians

5. The *hard* way would be to try and prove it.

   Here's an easier approach. If it is an identity, then it must be true for all values of x. Get out your calculator and see if it is true for some randomly chosen values of x. Try x = 17°. Try x = 39°. If the equation is true for x = 17°, then there is, maybe, a one percent chance that it is a conditional equation. If it also works for x = 39°, then you might bet your car that it's an identity. If it also works for x = 52.0082369°, you might bet the physical possession that is dearest to you (your *Life of Fred* books).

   By the way, there are *conditional* equations that work for x = 17, x = 39 and x = 52.0082369.

   Here's an example of one that works only for those three numbers:
$(x - 17)(x - 39)(x - 52.0082369) = 0$.

   Here's a conditional equation that works for every number except 4:
$$\frac{x^2 + 2x - 24}{x - 4} = x + 6.$$

   I have a friend who loves to wager. He'll bet on just about anything. He'll bet on whether the next car at the intersection is blue. He'll bet whether the judge rules in the defendant's favor. (He's a lawyer.) But he always begins with, "I'll bet you a nickel that. . . ."   Some big bets are okay. When you marry or choose a college major, you are making a larger bet. Here's the rule: Never wager your soul. Are there any exceptions to that rule?

Lesson Fifty-one
Law of Cosines

Do the *Your Turn to Play*.

Life of Fred:
Trigonometry
pp. 172–176

Problem 4 in the *Your Turn to Play* tells you when you will be using the law of cosines. Problem 3 in the *Your Turn to Play* tells you when nothing will work. If exactly two of the four items are angles, then you will use law of sines (which we haven't gotten to yet.)

In each of following, tell which of those three cases applies.

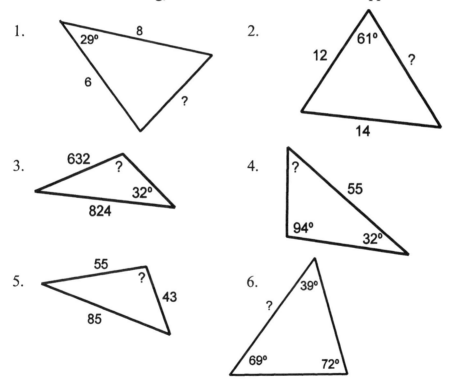

1. 29° 8 6 ?

2. 61° 12 ? 14

3. 632 ? 32° 824

4. ? 55 94° 32°

5. 55 ? 43 85

6. 39° ? 69° 72°

7. Find the value of the question mark in problem 1 above.
8. Find the value of the question mark in problem 2 above.
9. Find the value of the question mark in problem 4 above.
10. Find the value of the question mark in problem 5 above. (You'll either need to use trial and error or the $\cos^{-1}$ key to find the angle.)

1. Since only one of the four items is an angle, we would use law of cosines.

2. Since only one of the four items is an angle, we would use law of cosines.

3. Since two of the four items are angles, we will use law of sines.

4. This is a geometry question, not a trig question. Neither the law of cosines nor the law of sines will help you find the value of "?".

5. Since only one of the four items is an angle, we would use law of cosines.

6. Since three of the four items are angles, we don't have enough information to find the side.

7. (I'm replacing the "?" by an x.)

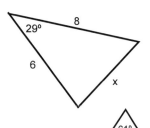

Law of cosines: $x^2 = 6^2 + 8^2 - 2(6)(8) \cos 29°$

$x^2 = 36 + 64 - 96(0.8746197)$

$x^2 = 16.036508$

$x = 4.0045609$

8.

Law of cosines: $14^2 = 12^2 + x^2 - 2(12)x \cos 61°$

$196 = 144 + x^2 - 24x(0.4848096)$

This isn't going to factor.

We'll use the quadratic formula. $x = \dfrac{-b \pm \sqrt{b^2 - 4ac}}{2a}$

First, put the equation in standard form. $ax^2 + bx + c = 0$

$x^2 - 11.635431x - 52 = 0$

$x = \dfrac{11.635431 \pm \sqrt{11.635431^2 - 4(1)(-52)}}{2}$

$x = \dfrac{11.635431 \pm 18.530603}{2}$ (We'll ignore the negative value of x.)

$x = 15.083017$

9. The angles of a triangle add to 180°. $x = 54°$

10. Law of cosines.

$85^2 = 55^2 + 43^2 - 2(55)(43) \cos x$

$2351 = -2(55)(43) \cos x$

$-0.4970401 = \cos x$ [x is in QII]

Entering -0.4970401 into my calculator and hitting the $\cos^{-1}$ key, I get $x = 119.80437°$.

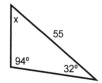

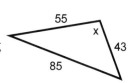

Lesson Fifty-two
The Handkerchief Problem

Set your clock and spend 16 minutes working on the Handkerchief Problem. Officially, you are not allowed to use the cos $^{-1}$ key. We will

Life of Fred:
Trigonometry
pp. 177–181

get to that in the next chapter. If you used the cos $^{-1}$ key, the problem would become toooooooo simple.

Lesson Fifty-three
Law of Sines

Do the *Your Turn to Play*.

Life of Fred:
Trigonometry
pp. 182–185

1. Find the value of x

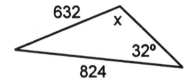

2. Two-or-three sentence essay question for English majors. Explain how you would go about finding the value of y. You do *not* have to do any computations for this problem.

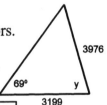

Intermission

Three pages ago I wrote, "Here's the rule: Never wager your soul. Are there any exceptions to that rule?"

Your soul = the innermost essence of who you are.

Hitler wagered his soul when he bet that God wasn't especially fond of Jewish people.

If you kill yourself, you are gambling.

If you live a regular American life—going to the movies, eating pizza, talking with your friends—you have placed your bet. You have wagered that life isn't worth any extreme effort—like, for example, Mother Theresa, who spent her life working with the poorest of the poor.

The truth is that *everyone* must wager his/her soul. It can't be avoided.

✸A✸N✸S✸W✸E✸R✸S✸

1. $\dfrac{632}{\sin 32^\circ} = \dfrac{824}{\sin x}$

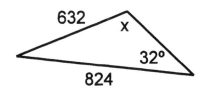

$\sin x = \dfrac{824 \sin 32^\circ}{632}$

$\sin x = \underline{0.6909074}$

Using trial and error:

We'll try x = 60°.	Then sin x = 0.8660254	Too big.
We'll try x = 45°	Then sin x = 0.7071068	Still too big.
We'll try x = 40°	Then sin x = 0.6427876	Too small.
We'll try x = 44°	Then sin x = 0.6946584	Close, but too big.
We'll try x = 43.8°	Then sin x = 0.6921432	Too big.
We'll try x = 43.6°	Then sin x = 0.6896195	Too small.

Or I could just enter 0.6909074 in my calculator and use the inverse sine function key ($\sin^{-1}$) and get x = 43.70198.

2.

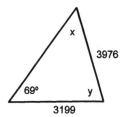

Essay: First, find x using the law of sines. Then using the fact that the sum of the angles of a triangle equals 180°, you find y.

Intermission

Rule: Never accept a rule just because it is written in a book.

Lesson Fifty-four
Proof of the Law of Cosines

Do the *Your Turn to Play.*

Life of Fred:
Trigonometry
pp. 186–187

Lesson Fifty-five
End of the Chapter—Review & Testing
Part One

Do all the problems in the first two cities.

 Elkton

Hanford

Life of Fred:
Trigonometry

The Cities starting
on p. 188

Lesson Fifty-six
End of the Chapter—Review & Testing
Part Two

Do all the problems in
the second pair of cities.

Odd answers are in
the text, and even
answers are
given here.

 Ralston

 Valley Falls

Life of Fred:
Trigonometry

The Cities starting
on p. 189

EVEN ANSWERS

Ralston
2. 0.9534892
4. 27.659948

Valley Falls
2. 31.716348 miles

4. Replacing $\dfrac{a}{\sin A}$ by $\dfrac{b}{\sin B}$ the formula Area $= \dfrac{a^2 \sin B \sin C}{2 \sin A}$

becomes Area $= \dfrac{ab \sin B \sin C}{2 \sin B} = \frac{1}{2} ab \sin C$ which is the formula we
used in the previous problem.

Do all the problems in
the third pair of cities.

Life of Fred:
Trigonometry

The Cities starting
on p. 190

 Waldorf

Dana

ANSWERS

Waldorf
1. 106.8 miles   2. Since the sum of the degrees of a triangle equals
180°, B = 71°.
3. 11.977 feet   4. We obtain a/sin A = c (since sin 90° = 1).
Rewriting this as sin A = a/c, we note that this is the definition
of sine (opposite over hypotenuse).

5. 10.318605 This was most easily found by finding the
supplement of the 121° and using the law of cosines. The
length of 3 in the problem is never used.

Dana
1. 6.28 inches
2. 266.9 miles. First find C = 180° − (73° + 38°).
3. cos x = 0.875; cos y = 0.0625
4. c = 8.5
5. You could compute all nine pieces of information. First, find x from
the small triangle on the left and the fact that the sum of the angles of a
triangle equals 180°. Next find y from the triangle with angles 58° and
40°. Find z from the triangle with angles 58° and 60°. Knowing angle x
and using the law of sines in the left triangle will give us the value of d.
Knowing angle y and using the law of sines in the 58°–40°–y triangle will
give us e. Knowing angle z and using the law of sines in the large triangle
will give us f. Then using the law of cosines or the law of sines will give
us g, h, and i.

Lesson Fifty-eight
Inverse Functions, One-to-one Functions

Do the **Exercises.**

Odd answers are in
the text, and even
answers are on the
next page.

Life of Fred:
Trigonometry
pp. 192–196

Lesson Fifty-nine
Definition of the Inverse Tangent Function

Do the *Your Turn to Play* on p. 199.
Do the *Your Turn to Play* on p. 200.

Life of Fred:
Trigonometry
pp. 197–200

Lesson Sixty
Principal Values of the Inverse Trig Functions

1. List four other spellings of Sin^{-1}.
2. The principal values of Sin^{-1} are
    $-90° \leq \text{Sin}^{-1}r \leq 90°$.

Life of Fred:
Trigonometry
pp. 201–205

Let's see if your calculator knows that fact.
Pick a value for r and punch in r followed by Sin^{-1}. Does your answer fall
in the interval between −90° and 90°?

For example, if I let r = 0.5, I will get $\text{Sin}^{-1} 0.5 = 30°$.

Do this a half dozen times.

Three questions:

A) Did it work?

B) What values of r will give you angles less than zero?

C) What values of r give you error messages?

3. What values of r will make $\text{Cos}^{-1}r$ negative?
4. What values of r will give error messages for $\text{Tan}^{-1}r$?

2. No g(3) = g(–3) = 81
4. yes
6. no   cos 30° = cos (–30°)
8. $f^{-1}(x) = 3x$
10. $h^{-1}(x) = (x + 15)^2$
12. $g^{-1}(x) = \sqrt[3]{4x - 2298}$

ANSWERS FOR LESSON 60

1. $\text{Sin}^{-1} \leftrightarrow \sin^{-1} \leftrightarrow \text{Arcsin} \leftrightarrow \text{arcsin} \leftrightarrow \text{Arc sin}$
2. A) *Did it work?* Yes. I have a smart calculator.

   B) *What values of r will give you angles less than zero?* Negative values of r gave me negative answers.

   C) *What values of r give you error messages?* If r was greater than one or less than minus one, I got an error message.

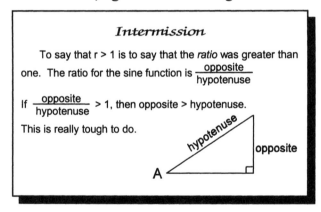

Intermission

To say that r > 1 is to say that the *ratio* was greater than one. The ratio for the sine function is $\dfrac{\text{opposite}}{\text{hypotenuse}}$

If $\dfrac{\text{opposite}}{\text{hypotenuse}} > 1$, then opposite > hypotenuse.

This is really tough to do.

3. No matter what values of r you use, $\text{Cos}^{-1}r$ will never be negative. (If you use r > 1 or r < – 1, you'll get error messages.)

4. Tan^{-1} is a function with a very large domain. It will accept any real number into its hopper.

Lesson Sixty-one
The Ambiguous Case for the Law of Sines

Do the *Your Turn to Plays.*

Life of Fred:
Trigonometry
pp. 206–210

Lesson Sixty-two
End of the Chapter—Review & Testing
Part One

Do all the problems in the first two cities.

Life of Fred:
Trigonometry

The Cities starting
on p. 211

 Elmwood

Santa Ana

Lesson Sixty-three
End of the Chapter—Review & Testing
Part Two

Do all the problems in
the second pair of cities.

Life of Fred:
Trigonometry

The Cities starting
on p. 212

Odd answers are in
the text, and even
answers are
given here.

 Tarheel

 Yuma

EVEN ANSWERS

Tarheel

2. You can't find d or e, but it's easy to find the angle opposite to side a.
It's just the complement of angle θ which was found in problem 1.

4. 5.3065997   6. 56/65

Yuma

2. $f(x) = x^4$ is not 1-1 since, for example, $f(-3)$ and $f(3)$ both equal 81. Hence f^{-1} is not a function. The easiest way to make it into a function is to restrict the domain of f to the non-negative real numbers. Then f is 1-1 and f^{-1} is a function.

4. Sin^{-1} has a domain equal to the real numbers *between –1 and 1* and is defined by the rule: Sin^{-1}(x), if x is positive, is found by first drawing a right triangle in which the hypotenuse is equal to one and one of the legs is equal to x. Then Sin^{-1}(x) equals the angle opposite the leg which has a length of x. If x is negative, then define Sin^{-1}(x) to equal Sin^{-1}(–x). For the case in which x = 1 (in which you can't draw a triangle) Sin^{-1}(1) = 90°. For the case in which x = 0, Sin^{-1}(0) = 0°.

6. –4/5

Lesson Sixty-four
End of the Chapter—Review & Testing
Part Three

Do all the problems in
the third pair of cities.

> *Life of Fred:*
> *Trigonometry*
> The Cities starting
> on p. 213

 Zeeland

Florissant

- -

Zeeland
1. 32°   2. 75°   3. 3.98
4. no solution. In solving by the law of sines, you get to sin A = 1.2349482 which is impossible.
5. 60°   6. $7/\sqrt{40}$ or $7/(2\sqrt{10})$ or $7\sqrt{10}/20$

Florissant
1. In the first two printings of *Life of Fred: Trig* we had sin(arcsin(sin(arcsin(cos(arccos(tan(arctan 8))))))). When we got to arccos 8, it couldn't be done. Substitute 0.8 for 8. Then the answer is 0.8
2. 61°   3. 80° or 100°
4. $2r^2 - 1$ 5. 5/3   6. 48°

Lesson Sixty-five
Polar Coordinates

Do the *Your Turn to Play*.

Life of Fred:
Trigonometry
pp. 215–221

Lesson Sixty-six
End of the Chapter—Review & Testing
Part One

Do all the problems in the first two cities.

Life of Fred:
Trigonometry
The Cities starting
on p. 222

Calvert

Ramona

Lesson Sixty-seven
End of the Chapter—Review & Testing
Part Two

Do all the problems in
the second pair of cities.

Life of Fred:
Trigonometry
The Cities starting
on p. 224

Odd answers are in
the text, and even
answers are
given here.

 Valparaiso

 Wales

✸E✸V✸E✸N✸ ✸A✸N✸S✸W✸E✸R✸S✸

Valparaiso

2.

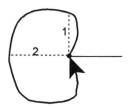

4. $(-7, -30°)$

Wales

2. The curve r = 5 cos 2θ looks like
It has all the symmetries: symmetry with   respect to the
pole, with respect to the polar axis and with   respect to the y axis.

4.

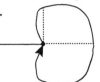

===

ℒesson 𝒮ixty-eight
End of the Chapter—Review & Testing
Part Three

Do all the problems in
the third pair of cities.

Life of Fred:
Trigonometry

The Cities starting
on p. 226

 Kalgary

 Lakewood

ⒶⓃⓈⓌⒺⓇⓈ

Kalgary

1.

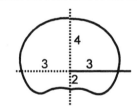

2. r = 27
3. (48.1, 26.7)
4. r sin θ = (3r/4) cos θ + 6
5. $(x - 0)^2 + (y - 4)^2 = 4^2$. The center is at (0, 4) and
the radius is equal to 4.

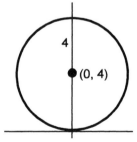

Lakewood
1. . . . .
2. no, no and no.
3. (5.4, 112°)
4. 12 leaves
5. The exact length is equal to 8.

Lesson Sixty-nine
One-to-one Correspondences

Life of Fred:
Trigonometry
pp. 227–231

1. To show that you have the same number of fingers on your right hand as you do on your left hand, you could count the fingers on each hand.

But that takes too much time. It's quicker to establish a 1-1 correspondence. How?

2. How many different 1-1 correspondences could you establish between {D, rainbow, #} and {$, motor, L}?

3. Let f:P → N be a function
   where P = {1, 2, 3, 4, 5, . . . } and
   where N = {–1, –2, –3, –4, –5, . . .} and
   where f(x) = –x.
   Is f a 1-1 correspondence?

4. Let g:P → W be a function
   where P = {1, 2, 3, 4, 5, . . . } and
   where W = {0, 1, 2, 3, 4, 5, . . . } and
   where g(x) = x – 1
   Is g a 1-1 correspondence?

5. Let set G be the set of all points on a graph, (a, b), where a and b are natural numbers N. (N = {1, 2, 3, 4, 5, 6, . . .}.)

G would look like ☞

with points going on forever toward the north and the east.

Some of the elements of G are (32, 9887), (1, 10000) and (23947392, 88).

Hard question: Is it possible to find a function h:G → N which is a one-to-one correspondence?

1. Touch thumb to thumb, index to index, etc.

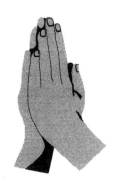

2. I count six ways:

1) D → $, rainbow → motor, # → L

2) D → motor, rainbow → $, # → L

3) D → L, rainbow → $, # → motor

4) D → $, rainbow → L, # → motor

5) D → motor, rainbow → L, # → $

6) D → L, rainbow → motor, # → $

3. f is 1-1 since no two elements of P (= {1, 2, 3, 4, . . . }) are mapped to the same element of N (= {–1, –2, –3, –4, . . .}).

f is onto N since every element of N is the image of some element in P. For example, –3987296 is an element of N. f(3987296) = –3987296.

Since f is both 1-1 and onto, it is a one-to-one correspondence.

There are the same number of positive integers as there are negative integers.

4. This is where things start to get a little weird. The function g is both 1-1 and onto and therefore, g is a one-to-one correspondence. We have just shown that there are the same number of positive integers as there are whole numbers.

5. Yup. It surprises a lot of people that there are as many ordered pairs of natural numbers as there are natural numbers. Here is one possible way that h might be defined:

h(1, 1) = 1
h(1, 2) = 2
h(2, 1) = 3
h(1, 3) = 4
h(2, 2) = 5
h(3, 1) = 6
h(1, 4) = 7
h(2, 3) = 8
h(3, 2) = 9
h(4, 1) = 10
h(1, 5) = 11
h(2, 4) = 12
h(3, 3) = 13
h(4, 2) = 14
h(5, 1) = 15
h(1, 6) = 16

Look at the pattern of the ordered pairs of numbers—(1, 1), (1, 2), (2, 1), . . . —and you can see that every ordered pair of natural numbers will be included.

Lesson Seventy

Numbers: Natural, Whole, Rational, Transcendental, Algebraic, and Real

1. Draw a Venn diagram which includes the irrational numbers and the transcendental numbers.

Life of Fred:
Trigonometry
pp. 232–top two-thirds of 241

2. Draw a Venn diagram which includes the algebraic numbers and the irrational numbers.

3. Using the definition of algebraic numbers, show that the cube root of four is algebraic.

4. Here is a proof. What fact is being proved?

    A) Assume there is a fraction a/b which when cubed equals 4.

    B) Reduce the fraction down to lowest terms so that a and b are not both even. (For example, 24/36 = 12/18 = 6/9.)

C) $(a/b)^3 = 4$	From line A
D) $a^3 = 4b^3$	Algebra
E) a^3 is even	Since it's equal to 4 times b^3.
F) a is even	The cubes of even numbers are even. The cubes of odd numbers are odd.
G) $a = 2c$ for some integer c.	Definition of an even number.
H) $(2c)^3 = 4b^3$	Lines D and G
I) $2c^3 = b^3$	Algebra
J) b^3 is even	Definition of an even number.
K) b is even	The cubes of even numbers are even. The cubes of odd numbers are odd.

    L) The assumption we made in line A is false since we arrived at a contradiction in lines B, F, and K.

5. Find the area of this sector.

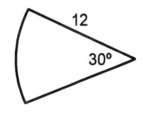

1.

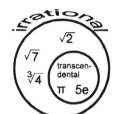

(All transcendental numbers are irrational, but not all irrational numbers are transcendental.)

2.

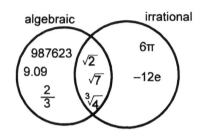

3. A number is algebraic if it is the root of an equation with integer coefficients. (Integers = { . . . –3, –2, –1, 0, 1, 2, 3, . . . })
$\sqrt[3]{4}$ is the root of $x^3 = 4$.

4. We have shown that $\sqrt[3]{4}$ is not a rational number.

5. The area of a sector is A = ½ $r^2\theta$ where θ is in radians.
Converting 30° to radians: $30° \times \dfrac{\pi}{180°} = \pi/6$.

Area = ½(12²)(π/6) = 12π

Lesson Seventy-one
Imaginary Numbers, Complex Numbers

Do the **Exercises** on p. 245.

Odd answers are in
the text, and even
answers are on the
next page.

Life of Fred:
Trigonometry
bottom third of p. 241–250

Lesson Seventy-two
The Barber's Paradox

Life of Fred:
Trigonometry
pp. 251–253

Intermission

Different people like different parts of mathematics. Some algebra students, for example, just love graphing. They can't get enough of it. Others, who are perhaps less artistically inclined, find it agony to draw a pair of axes.

Some adore computation. Give them lots of numbers and they are happy. Many of them balance their checkbooks twice each month.

A third group, find pleasure in thinking. They are happy to dispense with the art work and the arithmetic. Give them something small and neat that they can "chew on" for hours and they are content. This lesson is dedicated to that third group.

1. At the bottom of p. 253 was the sentence: "They found that it meant that you could never talk about the 'set of all sets.'" Call that set U (for the universal set). Why can't U exist?

2. If U did exist, would it be considered a normal set?

3. Can sets that are not normal exist?

2. $-10 - 3i$ 4. $-10 - 15i$ 6. 9   8. -1 10. $50 + 50i$
12. $20 + 30i$ 14. 104   16. $45 - 28i$ 18. $(29/25) + (22/25)i$

ANSWERS TO LESSON 72

1. Please don't read this until you've played with the question on your own for a long time (at least ten or fifteen minutes). In contrast, questions like $7 \times 8 = ?$ can be answered instantaneously. (= 56.)

Questions like "Why can't U exist?" are like eating a meal at a nice restaurant. You don't want to hurry the experience. (C.C. Coalback once bragged that he ate a $30 meal in five minutes.)

Suppose that the set of all sets (= U) exists. It is a very big set. U contains {4, ◨}, and it contains the set of all hoopoes. Since U is the set of all sets, U must contain every normal set and every set that is not normal. The sets {4, ◨} and the set of all hoopoes are normal sets (since neither of them contain themselves).

If U exists, then any subset of U exists. Consider the subset of U consisting of all normal sets. A Venn diagram would look like:

Hoopoe

the universal set U

normal sets	sets that are not normal

But the barber's paradox proves that the set of all normal sets can't exist.

2. If U (the set of all sets) existed, then U would contain every set. It would contain itself. Therefore, it would not be normal.

3. I gave an example of this. If M is the set of all sets mentioned in the book, then, since M itself is mentioned in the book, M must be a member of M.

An easier example: Let set B = {◨, ☺, ξ, B}. The set B is an element of B.

Lesson Seventy-three
r cis θ

Do the *Your Turn to Play*.

Life of Fred:
Trigonometry
pp. 254–256

Convert to algebraic form:
1. 7 cis 37°
2. 2 cis 30°   (Use the 30°–60°–90° triangle and give the exact answer.)

Lesson Seventy-four
de Moivre's Theorem

Do the *Your Turn to Play*.

Life of Fred:
Trigonometry
pp. 257–258

Do as many of these as you can in five minutes and then

1. $(2 \text{ cis } 10°)^6$
2. $(4 \text{ cis } 20°)^3$
3. $(30 \text{ cis } 15°)^4$
4. $(10 \text{ cis } 7°)^9$
5. $(15 \text{ cis } 100°)^5$
6. $(\xi \text{ cis } \theta)^8$
7. $(25 \text{ cis } 1°)^2$
8. $(5 \text{ cis } 55°)^7$
9. $(a \text{ cis } b)^{88}$
10. $(4 \text{ cis } \pi/6)^6$ (This one is in radians.)
11. $(11 \text{ cis } 80°)^4$

ANSWERS TO LESSON 73

1. $7 \text{ cis } 37° = 7 \cos 37° + 7i \sin 37°$ (by definition of cis)

2. 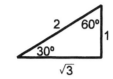 $2 \text{ cis } 30° = 2 \cos 30° + 2i \sin 30° = \sqrt{3} + i$

ANSWERS TO LESSON 74

1. $(2 \text{ cis } 10°)^6 = 2^6 \text{ cis } 60°$
2. $(4 \text{ cis } 20°)^3 = 4^3 \text{ cis } 60°$
3. $(30 \text{ cis } 15°)^4 = 30^4 \text{ cis } 60°$
4. $(10 \text{ cis } 7°)^9 = 10^9 \text{ cis } 63°$
5. $(15 \text{ cis } 100°)^5 = 15^5 \text{ cis } 500°$
6. $(\xi \text{ cis } \theta)^8 = \xi^8 \text{ cis } 8\theta$
7. $(25 \text{ cis } 1°)^2 = 625 \text{ cis } 2°$
8. $(5 \text{ cis } 55°)^7 = 5^7 \text{ cis } 385°$
9. $(a \text{ cis } b)^{88} = a^{88} \text{ cis } 88b$
10. $(4 \text{ cis } \pi/6)^6 = 4^6 \text{ cis } \pi$
11. $(11 \text{ cis } 80°)^4 = 11^4 \text{ cis } 320°$

Lesson Seventy-five
Proof of de Moivre's Theorem

Life of Fred:
Trigonometry
pp. 259–261

Do as many of these as you can in four minutes and then

Here's an example:

$(7 \text{ cis } 27°)^{1/15} =$

$7^{1/15} \text{ cis } (27° + k360°)/15$

where $k = 0, 1, 2, \ldots, 14$

1. $(2 \text{ cis } 10°)^{1/6}$
2. $(4 \text{ cis } 20°)^{1/3}$
3. $(30 \text{ cis } 15°)^{1/4}$
4. $(10 \text{ cis } 7°)^{1/9}$
5. $(15 \text{ cis } 100°)^{1/5}$
6. $(\xi \text{ cis } \theta)^{1/8}$
7. $(25 \text{ cis } 1°)^{1/2}$
8. $(5 \text{ cis } 55°)^{1/7}$
9. $(a \text{ cis } b)^{1/88}$
10. $(4 \text{ cis } \pi/6)^{1/6}$ (This one is in radians.)
11. $(11 \text{ cis } 80°)^{1/4}$

Lesson Seventy-six
Finding the nth Roots of Any Number

Do the *Your Turn to Play.*

Life of Fred:
Trigonometry
pp. 262–264

1. $(2 \text{ cis } 10°)^{1/6} = 2^{1/6} \text{ cis } (10° + k360°)/6$ where $k = 0, 1, \ldots, 5$

2. $(4 \text{ cis } 20°)^{1/3} = 4^{1/3} \text{ cis } (20° + k360°)/3$ where $k = 0, 1, 2$

3. $(30 \text{ cis } 15°)^{1/4} = 30^{1/4} \text{ cis } (15° + k360°)/4$ where $k = 0, 1, 2, 3$

4. $(10 \text{ cis } 7°)^{1/9} = 10^{1/9} \text{ cis } (7° + k360°)/9$ where $k = 0, 1, \ldots, 8$

5. $(15 \text{ cis } 100°)^{1/5} = 15^{1/5} \text{cis } (100° + k360°)/5$ where $k = 0, 1, 2, 3, 4$

6. $(\xi \text{ cis } \theta)^{1/8} = \xi^{1/8} \text{ cis } (\theta + k360°)/8$ where $k = 0, 1, \ldots, 7$

7. $(25 \text{ cis } 1°)^{1/2} = 5 \text{ cis } (1° + k360°)/2$ where $k = 0, 1$

8. $(5 \text{ cis } 55°)^{1/7} = 5^{1/7} \text{ cis } (55 + k360°)/7$ where $k = 0, 1, \ldots, 6$

9. $(a \text{ cis } b)^{1/88} = a^{1/88} \text{ cis } (b + 2k\pi)/88$ where $k = 0, 1, \ldots, 87$

10. $(4 \text{ cis } \pi/6)^{1/6} = 4^{1/6} \text{ cis } (\pi/6 + 2k\pi)/6$ where $k = 0, 1, \ldots, 5$

11. $(11 \text{ cis } 80°)^{1/4} = 11^{1/4} \text{ cis } (80° + k360°)/4$ where $k = 0, 1, 2, 3$

Lesson Seventy-seven
End of the Chapter—Review & Testing
Part One

Do all the problems in the first two cities.

Calvin

Elmer

Life of Fred:
Trigonometry

The Cities starting
on p. 265

Lesson Seventy-eight
End of the Chapter—Review & Testing
Part Two

Do all the problems in
the second pair of cities.

Odd answers are in
the text, and even
answers are
given here.

Upper Tract

Indio

Life of Fred:
Trigonometry

The Cities starting
on p. 266

EVEN ANSWERS

Upper Tract
2. 26^{50} cis 7869° or 5.6062×10^{70} cis 309°
4. 2 cis k120° where k = 0, 1, 2 or $2, -1 + i\sqrt{3}, -1 - i\sqrt{3}$

Indio
2. $11^{22}2^{11}$ cis 990° $\doteq -1.6671 \times 10^{26}$ i
4. $(i\sqrt{3})(2\sqrt{3} + 6i) = 6i - 6\sqrt{3} = -6\sqrt{3} + 6i = 12$ cis 150°
6. cis considered as a function from the ordered pairs (r, θ) to complex numbers is not 1-1 since different ordered pairs can yield the same image under the function. For example, (7, 30°) and (–7, 210°) are two different ordered pairs, but they are both mapped to 7 cis 30° and –7 cis 210° which are the same complex number.

Lesson Seventy-nine

End of the Chapter—Review & Testing

Part Three

Do all the problems in
the third pair of cities.

<table>
<tr><td>Life of Fred:
Trigonometry

The Cities starting
on p. 267</td></tr>
</table>

 Jamesport

Lambert

---

answers

Jamesport

1. $7i$ 2. 73^3 cis(arctan(8/3) × 6) $\doteq$ 389017 cis 56.66°

3. 2 cis $(36° + k72°)$ or -2 cis(k72°) where k = 0, 1, 2, 3, 4

4. $(4 + 4i)(-6 - 8i) = -24 - 32i - 24i + 32 = 8 - 56i =$
$\sqrt{3200}$ cis(arctan(-56/8)) $\doteq 40\sqrt{2}$ cis $-81.87° \doteq 40\sqrt{2}$ cis 278.13°

5. $4 + 4i = 4\sqrt{2}$ cis 45°
and $-6 - 8i \doteq 10$ cis 233.13°
$(4\sqrt{2}$ cis 45°)(10 cis 233.13°) = $40\sqrt{2}$ cis 278.13°

6. Using the lemma to de Moivre's theorem, 70 cis 61°

Lambert

1. $\sqrt{58}$ cis(arctan(7/3)) $\doteq$ 7.61577 cis 66.801°

2. $(\sqrt{29})^{14}$ cis(arctan(5/2) × 14) $\doteq 1.725 \times 10^{10}$ cis 234.78°

3. cis$(36° + k72°)$ where k = 0, 1, 2, 3, 4   4. $\sqrt{20}$ or $2\sqrt{5}$

5. Symmetry with respect to the x axis

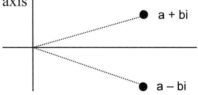

6. $\theta + \varphi > 90°$

7. That would mean that $\theta + \varphi > 180°$ which
is not possible if $0 < \theta < 90°$ and $0 < \varphi < 90°$.

104

Lesson Eighty
What You'll Need for Calculus
Chapter One: Functions

Do the *An Opportunity to Recall*.

Odd answers are in
the text, and even
answers are
given here. ⬛➡

Life of Fred:
Trigonometry
pp. 268–273

---

2. There are many possible answers. For example, the function could map everyone to orange.

A second example: map all males to brown and all females to purple.

Third example: map everyone who has a valid driver's license to orange and the rest to brown.

4. It is possible to have a function that is not 1-1. Map every element of the domain to Chris.

6. If $g(x) = 98x - \pi$, that says first multiply by 98 and then subtract π. g^{-1} is the function that would first add π and then divide by 98. Viz., $g^{-1}(x) = (x + \pi)/98$.

---

1. If $f{:}A \rightarrow B$ is a function and the range of f is B, must f be an onto function?

2. If we know that $f{:}A \rightarrow B$ is a function, must f be 1-1 in order that $f^{-1}{:}B \rightarrow A$ be a function?

3. If we know that $f{:}A \rightarrow B$ is a function, must f be onto B in order that $f^{-1}{:}B \rightarrow A$ be a function?

1. f:A → B means that the codomain of f is B. An onto function is a function in which every element of the codomain is an image of at least one element of the domain. The range of a function is the set of images. Since we are given that the range of f is B, every element in B must be "hit" by at least one element of A. Function f is onto.

2. If f were not 1-1, then two elements in A would be mapped onto the same image in B. For example, if ◆ and ★ were two different elements of A, then f(◆) = ✬ and f(★) = ✬, where ✬ is in B.

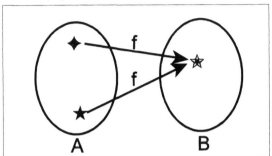

What would f⁻¹(✬) equal? It would have two different images. Then f⁻¹ couldn't be a function. (The definition of function is that every element in the domain—which is this case is B—must have *exactly one* image in the codomain.)

3. If f is not onto B, then there is some element of B that is not an image of an element of A. Suppose that ✪ were that element.

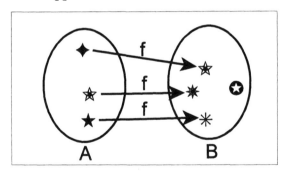

What would f⁻¹(✪) equal? It would have no image. Then f⁻¹ couldn't be a function. (The definition of function is that every element in the domain—which is this case is B—must have *exactly one* image in the codomain.)

Do the *An Opportunity to Recall.*

Odd answers are in
the text, and even
answers are
given here.

Life of Fred:
Trigonometry
pp. 274–278

2. $z^3 - 4z^2 - 3z + 12 = (z^2 - 3)(z - 4)$

4. $(4w + 7)(4w - 7)$

6. $(z - 4)(z^2 + 4z + 16)$

8. $y + 5 + 32/(y - 5)$

10. $\log_8 7$ is a real number. Hence it is a polynomial—just as 5 would be considered a polynomial since it is the combination of variables and real numbers using addition and multiplication. If you like, we might write the polynomial 5 as $5x^0$ or as $5 + 0x$. Then it might look more polynomialish.*

The same is true for sin 43.8997°. The other two expressions can't be formed using addition and multiplication of real numbers and variables.

12. $y = 3x^4 - 5x + 2$.

Here are some points (rounded off): (–2, 60), (–1, 10), (–0.5, 4.7), (0, 2), (0.1, 1.5), (0.2, 1), (0.3, 0.5), (0.4, 0), (0.7, –0.8), (1, 0), (2, 40)

14. $30 < x < 50$

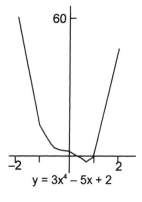

$y = 3x^4 - 5x + 2$

---

* Sorry about that. English majors who are reading this book probably winced when they read that. I guess I could have written, "Then it might look more like a polynomial." But that wouldn't have been as much *fun*.

Lesson Eighty-two

What You'll Need for Calculus
Chapter Three: Speed

Do the *An Opportunity to Recall.*

Odd answers are in
the text, and even
answers are
given here. ➡

Life of Fred:
Trigonometry
pp. 279

---

2. A) Your speed couldn't have been always less than 60 mph during the entire trip since that would imply that your average speed couldn't have been 60 mph. Your speed couldn't have been always greater than 60 mph during the entire trip since that would imply that your average speed was greater than 60 mph. In going from less than 60 mph to greater than 60 mph, you must have at some point traveled at exactly 60 mph.

4. $\Delta y = 23 - 17 = 6$ feet.

$\Delta t = 2$ seconds.

Average speed $= \Delta y / \Delta t = 3$ feet/sec.

---

1. The Greek capital letter delta, Δ, stands for "change in." Let x equal the amount of money you have in your checking account. Before you deposit your paycheck, x = $230. Your paycheck is $80. What is Δx?

2. Let y equal the number of sticks of gum you have in your pocket. You share a third of them with your friend Dale. What is Δy?

3. You are working as a cashier at Stanthony's PieOne pizza place. In three hours, you ring up $60. Let d = dollars rung up and let t = time.

A) What does $\dfrac{\Delta d}{\Delta t}$ equal?

B) What does $\dfrac{\Delta d}{\Delta t}$ represent?

4. If the temperature of your room was 66° and later it was 72°, at some point it must have been exactly 71°. If you had $54 on Friday and $66 on Monday, at some point you *need not have had* exactly $64. What's the difference between this and the temperature example?

1. $\Delta x = \$80$.

2. You started out with y sticks of gum. After sharing you had (⅔)y. Therefore the change in the number of sticks of gum is (−⅓)y. It is negative since your number of sticks of gum went down.

3. A) $\dfrac{\Delta d}{\Delta t} = \dfrac{\$60}{3 \text{ hrs.}} = \$20/\text{hr.}$

   B) $\dfrac{\Delta d}{\Delta t}$ represents the average amount of money per hour that you have rung up on your register.

4. Temperature is a continuous variable. To go from a lower temperature to a higher one, you pass through every intermediate temperature. Money is a discrete variable. It comes in chunks. $54.00 is followed by $54.01, by $54.02, by $54.03. You can't have $54.01⅝. The number of children is a discrete variable. If you had two children and now you have five, this does not mean that at some point in time you had 3⅝ kids.

Lesson Eighty-three

What You'll Need for Calculus
Chapter Four: Slope

Do the *An Opportunity to Recall.*

Odd answers are in
the text, and even
answers are
given here.

Life of Fred:
Trigonometry
pp. 280–281

2. The tangent is horizontal so the slope is equal to zero.

4.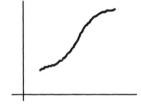

6. $13 = (y - 2)/(x + 7)$

8. $x^3 + 3x^2(7y) + 3x(7y)^2 + (7y)^3$

1. Expand $(x + \Delta x)^3$.

Note: we write the cube of Δx as $(\Delta x)^3$.*

2. The expansion of $(a + b)^{88}$

$$= a^{88} + \frac{88}{1}\, a^{87}b + \frac{88 \cdot 87}{2 \cdot 1}\, a^{86}b^2 + \frac{88 \cdot 87 \cdot 86}{3!}\, a^{85}b^3 + \text{etc.}$$

Give the first five terms in the expansion of $(x + \Delta x)^9$.

[The expansion of $(x + \Delta x)^n$ is the main use of the binomial formula in calculus.]

✱ $(\Delta x)^3$ is the cube of the change in x. On the other hand, Δx^3 means the change in the value of x^3.

1. $(x + \Delta x)^3 = x^3 + 3x^2 \Delta x + 3x(\Delta x)^2 + (\Delta x)^3$.

2. The first five terms in the expansion of $(x + \Delta x)^9$

$$x^9 + 9x^8 \Delta x + \frac{9 \cdot 8}{2} x^7(\Delta x)^2 + \frac{9 \cdot 8 \cdot 7}{6} x^6(\Delta x)^3 + \frac{9 \cdot 8 \cdot 7 \cdot 6}{24} x^5(\Delta x)^4$$

Lesson Eighty-four
What You'll Need for Calculus
Chapter Five: Derivatives

Do the *An Opportunity to Recall*.

Odd answers are in
the text, and even
answers are
given here.

> *Life of Fred:*
> *Trigonometry*
> pp. 282–283

2. Yes.

4.

6. That's equal to one because of the zero exponent.

8. [10, 50]

Lesson Eighty-five

What You'll Need for Calculus
Chapter Six: Concavity

Do the *An Opportunity to Recall*.

Odd answers are in
the text, and even
answers are
given here.

Life of Fred:
Trigonometry
pp. 284–286

2.

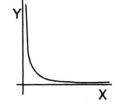

4.

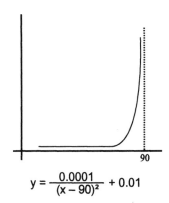

$$y = \frac{0.0001}{(x - 90)^2} + 0.01$$

 This curve has a vertical asymptote at x = 90. When x gets close to 90, the value of y explodes.

 This is the actual curve which Fred will use in chapter six in calculus when he invests in Data Atomic Scholarship stock.

6. $2\pi + 28$ ft.
8. 328.1 ft.

What You'll Need for Calculus
Chapter Seven: Trig

Do the *An Opportunity to Recall*.

Odd answers are in
the text, and even
answers are
given here.

Life of Fred:
Trigonometry
pp. 287–289

2. $3\pi/4$ 4. $\pi = 180°$ 6. $\pi/12 \times 180°/\pi = 15°$ 8. y
10. $\sqrt{108} = \sqrt{36}\ \sqrt{3} = 6\sqrt{3}$

Lesson Eight-seven

What You'll Need for Calculus
Chapters Eight and Nine:
Related Rates, Curvature, Mean Value Theorem, Acceleration

Do the *An Opportunity to Recall*.

Odd answers are in
the text, and even
answers are
given here.

Life of Fred:
Trigonometry
pp. 290–292

2. k = 1280   4. k = 60

1. Given a Texas-sized cherry. Diameter = 6". What is the
volume and what is the surface area?
2. We decided to make that Texas-sized cherry into a fruit
pizza and smashed it down into the shape of a disk that was 1" high. What
would be the diameter of that creation?

✸A✸N✸S✸W✸E✸R✸S✸

1. diameter = 6". radius = 3". $V = (4/3)\pi r^3 = (4/3)\pi 3^3 = 36\pi$ cubic inches. Surface area = $4\pi r^2 = 4\pi 3^2 = 36\pi$ square inches.

2. From the previous problem we know that the volume of the cherry is 36π cubic inches. We need to find the dimensions of a cylinder whose height is 1" and whose volume is 36π cubic inches.

The formula for the volume of a cylinder is $V = \pi r^2 h$ where V is the volume, r is a radius and h is the height. In this case, we know that h = 1".

$$36\pi = \pi r^2(1)$$
$$36 = r^2$$
$$6 = r \qquad \text{(We don't use } r = \pm 6 \text{ in this}$$
case since the radius of a cylinder is a positive number.)

12" = diameter. (Probably this would be a dessert pizza which normally follows a main-course pizza.)

═══════════════════════════════════════

Lesson Eighty-eight
What You'll Need for Calculus
Chapters Ten and Eleven:
Integrals, Area, Parametric Forms, Improper Integrals

───────────────────────────────────────

Do the *An Opportunity to Recall*.

> *Life of Fred:*
> *Trigonometry*
> pp. 293–top half of 295

The odd answer is in the text, and the even answer is given here. ◢

═══════════════════════════════════════

2. Raise each equation to the two-thirds power: $x^{2/3} = \cos^2 \theta$
$y^{2/3} = \sin^2 \theta$

Add them together: $x^{2/3} + y^{2/3} = 1$

114

Lesson Eighty-nine
What You'll Need for Calculus
Chapter Twelve and Thirteen:
Work, Solids of Rotation, Torque, Centroids,
Averages, Integration by Parts, Moment of Inertia

Do the *An Opportunity to Recall.*

Odd answers are in
the text, and even
answers are
given here.

Life of Fred:
Trigonometry
pp. 295–298

2.

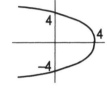

1. Let's have some fun. (Is that allowed in a math book?)
And let's check your artistic skills. Suppose we take Fred
and make him into a solid of rotation. Rotate around the back
of his head. It wouldn't be surprising if your drawing is better
than mine.

2. What is the value of ω for the minute hand of a clock?

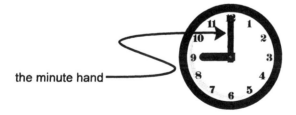

the minute hand

3. Does the size of a clock make a difference for ω for the minute hand?

4. In elementary school you learned how to take the average of a set of
numbers. The average of 6, 8 and 10 is $(6 + 8 + 10)/3 = 8$. In chapter
thirteen in calculus we will take the average of an infinite number of
numbers. Graph $y = x^2$ for $0 \le x \le 2$. *Guess* what the average height of
that curve above the x-axis is.

1.

2. ω is angular speed which is the change in θ with respect to time. The angular speed of a minute hand is 360° per hour.

In calculus the formulas for taking derivatives (whatever that means!) are only good when the angle is in radians. That's why we introduced radians in *Life of Fred: Trigonometry.*

So, for calculus, we would say that ω = 2π per hour.

3. Nope.

4.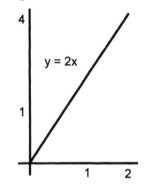

If we were graphing a straight line, then estimating the average height would be pretty straightforward. The average height would be equal to 2.

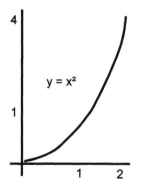

But y = x² is below y = 2x (except at the endpoints). So its average height will be less than 2.

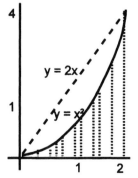

In chapter thirteen we will be able to show that the average of the infinite number of dotted vertical lines is equal to 1⅓.

Lesson Ninety

What You'll Need for Calculus
Chapter Fourteen: Logs

Do the *An Opportunity to Recall*.

Odd answers are in
the text, and even
answers are
given here. ◀

Life of Fred:
Trigonometry
Bottom of p. 298–299

---

2. 2

4. 1

6. $\log_{67} 67^{-1}$ which is equal to -1

8. 1

10. $\log_8 64$ which is 2.

---

1. $\log_8 2$

2. $\log_6 4 + \log_6 9$

3. $(\log_8 9)(\log_9 329)$

4. $\log_1 17$

5. Express as a single logarithm $\dfrac{\ln 33}{\ln 11}$

6. In calculus when we find the derivative of $y = \log_b x$,
   on one line we will have $\Delta y = \log_b (x + \Delta x) - \log_b x$.
   On the next line we have $\Delta y = \log_b (x + \Delta x)/x$.

Which law of logs was used?   [Note: In the calculus text this is done without giving a reason. One of the prerequisites for calculus is knowing the four laws of logarithms.]

7. Later on the same page we go from
   $$\Delta y/\Delta x = (1/x)(x/\Delta x) \log_b (1 + \Delta x/x)$$
   to $\Delta y/\Delta x = (1/x)\log_b (1 + \Delta x/x)^{(x/\Delta x)}$.
   What law of logs was used?

✸A✸N✸S✸W✸E✸R✸S✸

1. $\log_8 2 = \log_8 (2^3)^{1/3} = \log_8 8^{1/3} = (1/3) \log_8 8 = 1/3$

2. $\log_6 4 + \log_6 9 = \log_6 36 = 2$

3. $(\log_8 9)(\log_9 329) = \log_8 329$ Using the change-of-base law in the form: $\log_c a = (\log_c b)(\log_b a)$

4. $\log_1 17$ asks the question: $1^? = 17$.   This has no answer. You can't have 1 as the base of a logarithm.

5. $\dfrac{\ln 33}{\ln 11} = \dfrac{\log_e 33}{\log_e 11} = \log_{11} 33$ By the change-of-base rule.

6. To go from $\Delta y = \log_b (x + \Delta x) - \log_b x$

     to $\Delta y = \log_b (x + \Delta x)/x$

we used the quotient rule: $\log (m/n) = \log m - \log n$

7. To go from $\Delta y/\Delta x = (1/x)(x/\Delta x) \log_b (1 + \Delta x/x)$

     to $\Delta y/\Delta x = (1/x)\log_b (1 + \Delta x/x)^{(x/\Delta x)}$

we used the birdie rule: $\log m^n = n \log m$.

118

Lesson Ninety-one

What You'll Need for Calculus
Chapter Fifteen: Conics and Hydrostatic Force

Do the *An Opportunity to Recall*.

Odd answers are in
the text, and even
answers are
given here.

*Life of Fred:
Trigonometry*
pp. 300–302

2. $y - 6 = 4(2/4)(x - (-3))^2$ An upward-pointing parabola with vertex at $(-3, 6)$ where the distance from the vertex to focus is 1/2.

4. Ellipse with center at (5, –7).
Semiminor axis (horizontal) = 6.
Semimajor axis (vertical) = 10.

6. An hyperbola with center (5, –7).

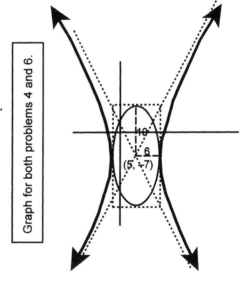

Graph for both problems 4 and 6.

8. Circle with center (–6, –40) and
radius = $\sqrt{37}$

119

Lesson Ninety-two
What You'll Need for Calculus
Chapter Sixteen: Infinite Series

Do the *An Opportunity to Recall.*

Odd answers are in
the text, and even
answers are
given here.

> *Life of Fred:*
> *Trigonometry*
> pp. 303

2. $\sqrt{2} + \sqrt[3]{3} + \sqrt[4]{4} + \sqrt[5]{5}$

4. $a(x_1 + x_2) = ax_1 + ax_2$ is the distributive law.

1. In chapter sixteen in calculus, Fred, the scarecrow, and the tin-wood duck were competing with each other to tell what they called "long-time stories." Those are stories in which the action of the story takes a long time to complete.

The tin-wood duck began with a very short story: "A snail crawled around the world." The duck figured this would take almost forever to do. If snails take about an hour to travel an inch and if the circumference of the earth is 25,000 miles, find out how long (in years) it would take the snail.

2. Fred told the story about how Jacob loved the fair maiden Fredrika and how long it took him to obtain the permission of Fredrika's father to marry her.

At one point in his story he has the equation $\sum_{i=1}^{n} \frac{1}{10000i} = 1.$

In the next sentence he has $\frac{1}{10000} \sum_{i=1}^{n} \frac{1}{i} = 1.$

What law of algebra allowed him to do this?

✸A✸N✸S✸W✸E✸R✸S✸

1. We start with $\dfrac{1 \text{ hr}}{1 \text{ in}}$ and then we'll multiply by the conversion factors to convert this into years per trip. Note that each conversion factor (each fraction) is equal to one since the numerator equals the denominator).

$$\dfrac{1 \text{ hr}}{1 \text{ in}} \ \dfrac{12 \text{ in}}{1 \text{ foot}} \ \dfrac{5280 \text{ ft}}{1 \text{ mile}} \ \dfrac{25000 \text{ miles}}{1 \text{ trip around the equator}} \ \dfrac{1 \text{ day}}{24 \text{ hours}} \ \dfrac{1 \text{ year}}{365 \text{ days}} \approx$$

$$\dfrac{180,800 \text{ years}}{1 \text{ trip around the equator}}$$

Note how the dimensions cancel, leaving us with years per trip:

$$\dfrac{1 \text{ hr}}{1 \text{ in}} \ \dfrac{12 \text{ in}}{1 \text{ foot}} \ \dfrac{5280 \text{ ft}}{1 \text{ mile}} \ \dfrac{25000 \text{ miles}}{1 \text{ trip around the equator}} \ \dfrac{1 \text{ day}}{24 \text{ hours}} \ \dfrac{1 \text{ year}}{365 \text{ days}}$$

2. $\displaystyle\sum_{i=1}^{n} \dfrac{1}{10000i}$ means $\dfrac{1}{10000} + \dfrac{1}{10000\cdot2} + \dfrac{1}{10000\cdot3}$

$$+ \ \dfrac{1}{10000\cdot4} + \dfrac{1}{10000\cdot5} + \ldots + \dfrac{1}{10000\cdot n}$$

If we factor $\dfrac{1}{10000}$ out of each term (using the distributive law) we

obtain $\dfrac{1}{10000} \left(\dfrac{1}{1} + \dfrac{1}{2} + \dfrac{1}{3} + \dfrac{1}{4} + \dfrac{1}{5} + \ldots + \dfrac{1}{n} \right)$

which is $\dfrac{1}{10000} \displaystyle\sum_{i=1}^{n} \dfrac{1}{i}$

Lesson Ninety-three

What You'll Need for Calculus
Chapters Seventeen and Eighteen:
Solids of Revolution, Trig Substitutions, Surface Area,
Polar Coordinates, Alternating Series, Power Series

Do the *An Opportunity to Recall.*

The odd answer is in the
text, and the even answer
is given here. ◀▌

Life of Fred:
Trigonometry
pp. 304–305

---

2. For repeated quadratic factors we would make $\dfrac{2x^2 + 3}{(x^2 + 1)^2}$ equal to

$\dfrac{Ax + B}{(x^2 + 1)} + \dfrac{Cx + D}{(x^2 + 1)^2}$

Multiply through by $(x^2 + 1)^2$ to eliminate the denominators:

$2x^2 + 3 = (Ax + B)(x^2 + 1) + Cx + D$

$2x^2 + 3 = Ax^3 + Ax + Bx^2 + B + Cx + D$

From advanced algebra we know that if an equation is true for all values of x, then corresponding coefficients of x are equal.

The coefficients of x^3:	$0 = A$	
The coefficients of x^2:	$2 = B$	
The coefficients of x:	$0 = A + C$	
The coefficients of x^0:	$3 = B + D$	$\dfrac{2x^2 + 3}{(x^2 + 1)^2} = \dfrac{2}{x^2 + 1} + \dfrac{1}{(x^2 + 1)^2}$

---

1. In chapter eighteen of calculus we will do graphing of polar equations. Graph the polar equation r = 5. What would be the equivalent form in rectangular coordinates?

2. Using point-plotting, graph $r = \dfrac{1}{1 - \sin \theta}$

1. This would be all points 5 units away from the pole.

In rectangular coordinates, a circle with center
at the origin and a radius of 5 is given by the
equation $x^2 + y^2 = 25$.

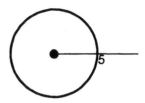

2. $r = \dfrac{1}{1 - \sin \theta}$

   To point-plot, we take various values of θ and find the corresponding
values of r.
   (We could have taken various values of r and found the corresponding
values of θ, but that would be a lot more work.)

Here are some values of θ

0°	30°	60°	90°	–30°	–60°	–90°	120°	150°

and their corresponding values of r

1	2	7.5	∞	0.67	0.54	0.5	7.5	2

Plotting these points

and connecting the dots
gives us a parabola.

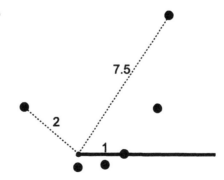

Lesson Ninety-four
What You'll Need for Calculus
Chapters Nineteen through Twenty-four:
Hyperbolic Trig, Separating the Variables, Numerical Integration, Vectors, Partial Derivatives, Double Integrals, Vector Calculus

---

> *Life of Fred:*
> *Trigonometry*
> pp. 306–309

Just read and enjoy.

These last six chapters of *Life of Fred: Calculus* won't bring up anything from arithmetic/algebra/geometry/trig that we haven't already covered and reviewed.

Here's a cake for you.

You are cleared and ready for takeoff to calculus.

Index

If you would like to
learn more about
books written about
Fred . . .

FredGauss.com

UNIVERSITY MATHEMATICS

Life of Fred: Calculus

Functions, Limits, Speed, Slope, Derivatives, Concavity, Trig, Related Rates, Curvature, Integrals, Area, Work, Centroids, Logs, Conics, Infinite Series, Solids of Revolution, Polar Coordinates, Hyperbolic Trig, Vectors, Partial Derivatives, Double Integrals, Vector Calculus, Differential Equations. (Two years of college calculus.)

ISBN: 978-0-9709995-0-4, hardback, 544 pages. $39   Answer key, paper, $6

Life of Fred: Statistics

Descriptive Statistics (averages, measures of dispersion, types of distributions), Probability, Bayes' Theorem, From a Given Population Determine What Samples Will Look Like (7 tests), Techniques of Sampling, From a Given Sample Determine What the Population Was (14 tests), Determine Whether Two Given Samples Came From the Same Population (15 tests), Working With Three or More Samples (10 tests), Emergency Statistics Guide, Regression Equations, Field Guide, 16 Tables. (College level.)

ISBN: 978-0-9709995-5-9, hardback, 544 pages. $39   Answer key, paper, $6

Life of Fred: Linear Algebra

Solving systems of equations with one, many, and no solutions. Gauss-Jordan elimination. Gaussian elimination. Matrices. *LU*-decomposition. Vector spaces. Inner product spaces. Gram-Schmidt orthogonalization process. Fourier series. Data fitting. Linear Transformations. Linear functionals. Dual spaces. Eigenvalues and eigenvectors. Markov chains.   (Upper-division college level.)

ISBN: 978-0-9791072-1-4, hardback, 352 pages. $49   Answer key, paper, $6

To order: visit   PolkaDotPublishing.com